THE BEST CAT STORIES

The Best Cat Stories

Selected by

JOHN MONTGOMERY

Illustrated by

JANET and ANNE GRAHAME-JOHNSTONE

UNABRIDGED

PAN BOOKS LTD · LONDON

First published 1969 by Pan Books Ltd,
33 Tothill Street, London, S.W.1
330 02417 5

Printed in Great Britain by
Cox & Wyman Ltd, London, Reading and Fakenham

CONTENTS

ACKNOWLEDGEMENTS

C. Day-Lewis: CAT; Mr C. Day-Lewis, CBE, and A. D. Peters & Co.

Hilaire Belloc: A CONVERSATION WITH A CAT; A. D. Peters & Co.

Sandy Wilson: THIS IS SYLVIA from *This is Sylvia: Her Lives and Loves*; by permission of Mr Sandy Wilson and his agent, Joan Rees Ltd.

Damon Runyon: LILLIAN from *Guys and Dolls*; the executors of the estate of the late Damon Runyon.

Q. Patrick: THE FAT CAT; Curtis Brown.

W. W. Jacobs: THE WHITE CAT from *Captains All*; The Society of Authors, representing the estate of the author.

Christabel Aberconway: THE CAT AND THE CHILD; The Dowager Lady Aberconway.

John Pudney: KITTY, KITTY, KITTY; the author, and David Higham Associates.

M. R. James: THE STALLS OF BARCHESTER CATHEDRAL from *The Collected Stories of M. R. James*; Edward Arnold (Publishers) Ltd.

Compton Mackenzie: NO 25 TO BE LET OR SOLD from *Our Street*; the author and Hughes Massie Ltd.

Margery Sharp: THE AMETHYST CAT; Miss Margery Sharp and A. D. Peters & Co.

Jan Struther: THE CATS.

Margaret Benson: THE SOUL OF A CAT; William Heinemann Ltd.

Michael Joseph: MINNA MINNA MOWBRAY from *Cat's Company*; The Hon. Mrs Joseph.

Buster Lloyd-Jones: MY CATS from *The Animals Came in One By One*; the author, and Martin Secker and Warburg Ltd.

P. G. Wodehouse: THE STORY OF WEBSTER from *Mulliner Nights*; Herbert Jenkins Ltd.

John Montgomery: THE CHRISTMAS CAT from *The Christmas Cat*; George Allen & Unwin Ltd.

EDITOR'S FOREWORD

This must be the first time in the history of English literature that an anthology of stories has been able to include a new poem, hitherto unpublished, by the Poet Laureate.

I am greatly indebted to Mr C. Day-Lewis for so kindly writing his poem CAT for first publication in this volume.

I also thank the Dowager Lady Aberconway for her help and encouragement, and for writing me a new story, THE CAT AND THE CHILD.

J.M.

Cat

Tearaway kitten or staid mother of fifty,
Persian, Chinchilla, Siamese
Or backstreet brawler – you all have a tiger in your blood
And eyes opaque as the sacred mysteries.

The hunter's instinct sends you pouncing, dallying,
Formal and wild as a temple dance.
You take from man what is your due – the fireside saucer,
And give him his – a purr of tolerance.

Like poets you wrap your solitude around you
And catch your meaning unawares:
With consequential tail or frantic tarantella
You follow up your top-secret affairs.

Simpkin, our portly cat, assumes my lap
As a princess her rightful throne,
Purrs round and drops asleep there. Each is a familiar
Warmth to the other, each no less alone.

C. Day Lewis

Cat

by C. Day-Lewis

Tearaway kitten or staid mother of fifty,
Persian, Chinchilla, Siamese
Or backstreet brawler – you all have a tiger in your blood
And eyes opaque as the sacred mysteries.

The hunter's instinct sends you pouncing, dallying,
Formal and wild as a temple dance.
You take from man what is your due – the fireside saucer,
And give him his – a purr of tolerance.

Like poets you wrap your solitude around you
And catch your meaning unawares:
With consequential trot or frantic tarantella
You follow up your top-secret affairs.

Simpkin, our pretty cat, assumes my lap
As a princess her rightful throne,
Pads round and drops asleep there. Each is a familiar
Warmth to the other, each no less alone.

A Conversation With a Cat

by HILAIRE BELLOC

THE other day I went into the bar of a railway station and, taking a glass of beer, I sat down at a little table by myself to meditate upon the necessary but tragic isolation of the human soul. I began my meditation by consoling myself with the truth that something in common runs through all nature, but I went on to consider that this cuts no ice, and that the heart needed something more. I might by long research have discovered some third term a little less hackneyed than these two, when fate, or some good influence or accident, or the ocean and my fostering star, sent me a tawny, silky, long-haired cat.

If it be true that nations have the cats they deserve, then the English people deserve well in cats, for there are none so prosperous or so friendly in the world. But even for an English cat this cat was exceptionally friendly and fine – especially friendly. It leapt at one graceful bound into my lap, nestled there, put out an engaging right front paw to touch my arm with a pretty timidity by way of introduction, rolled up at me an eye of bright but innocent affection, and then smiled a secret smile of approval.

No man could be so timid after such an approach as not to make some manner of response. So did I. I even took the liberty of stroking Amathea (for by that name did I receive this vision), and though I began this gesture in a respectful fashion, after the best models of polite deportment with strangers, I was soon lending it some warmth, for I was touched to find that I had a friend; yes, even here, at the end of the tube in SW99. I proceeded (as is right) from caress to speech, and said, 'Amathea, most beautiful of cats, why have you deigned to single me out for so much favour? Did you recognize in me a friend to all that breathes, or were you yourself suffering from loneliness (though I take it you are near your own dear home), or is there pity in the hearts of animals as there is in the hearts of some humans? What, then, was your motive? Or am I, indeed, foolish to ask, and not rather to take whatever good comes to me in whatever way from the gods?'

To these questions, Amathea answered with a loud purring noise, expressing with closed eyes of ecstasy her delight in the encounter.

'I am more than flattered, Amathea,' said I, by way of answer; 'I am consoled. I did not know that there was in the world anything breathing and moving, let alone one so tawny-perfect, who would give companionship for its own sake and seek out, through deep feeling, some one companion out of all living kind. If you do not address me in words I know the reason and I commend it; for in words lie the seeds of all dissension, and love at its most profound is silent. At least, I read that in a book, Amathea; yes, only the other day. But I confess that the book told me nothing of those gestures which are better than words, or of that caress which I continue to bestow upon you with all the gratitude of my poor heart.'

To this Amathea made a slight gesture of acknowledgement – not disdainful – wagging her head a little, and then settling it down in deep content.

'Oh, beautiful-haired Amathea, many have praised you before you found me to praise you, and many will praise you, some in your own tongue, when I am no longer held in the bonds of your presence. But none will praise you more sincerely. For there is not a man living who knows better than I that the four charms of a cat lie in its closed eyes, its long and lovely hair, its silence, and even its affected love.'

But at the word affected Amathea raised her head, looked up at me tenderly, once more put forth her paw to touch my arm, and then settled down again to a purring beatitude.

'*You* are secure,' said I sadly; 'mortality is not before you. There is in your complacency no foreknowledge of death nor even of separation. And for that reason, Cat, I welcome you the more. For if there has been given to your kind this repose in common living, why, then, we men also may find it by following your example and not considering too much what may be to come and not remembering too much what has been and will never return. Also, I thank you, for this, Amathea, my sweet Euplokamos' (for I was becoming a little familiar through an acquaintance of a full five minutes and from the absence of all recalcitrance), 'that you have reminded me of my youth, and in a sort of shadowy way, a momentary way, have restored it to me. For there is an age, a blessed youthful age (O My Cat) even with the miserable race of men, when all things are consonant with the life of the body, when sleep is regular and long and deep, when enmities are either unknown or a subject for rejoicing, and when the whole of being is lapped in hope as you are now lapped on my lap, Amathea. Yes, we also, we of the doomed race, know peace. But whereas you possess it from blind kittenhood to that last dark day, so mercifully short with you, we grasp it only for a very little while. But I would not sadden you by the mortal plaint. That would be treason indeed, and a vile return for your goodness. What! When you have chosen me out of seven London millions upon whom to confer the tender solace of the heart, when you have proclaimed yourself so suddenly to be my dear, shall I introduce you to the sufferings of those of whom you know nothing save that they feed you, house you, and pass you by? At least you do not take us for gods, as do the dogs, and the more am I humbly beholden to you for this little service of recognition – and something more.'

Amathea slowly raised herself upon her four feet, arched her back, yawned, looked up at me with a smile sweeter than ever and then went round and round, preparing for herself a new couch upon my coat, whereon she settled and began once more to purr in settled ecstasy.

Already had I made sure that a rooted and anchored

affection had come to me from out the emptiness and nothingness of the world and was to feed my soul henceforward; already had I changed the mood of long years and felt a conversion towards the life of things, an appreciation, a cousinship with the created light – and all that through one new link of loving kindness – when whatever it is that dashes the cup of bliss from the lips of mortal man (Tupper) up and dashed it good and hard. It was the Ancient Enemy who put the fatal sentence into my heart, for we are the playthings of the greater powers, and surely some of them are evil.

'You will never leave me, Amathea,' I said; 'I will respect your sleep and we will sit here together through all uncounted time, I holding you in my arms and you dreaming of the fields of Paradise. Nor shall anything part us, Amathea; you are my cat and I am your human. Now and onwards into the fullness of peace.'

Then it was that Amathea lifted herself once more, and with delicate, discreet, unweighted movement of perfect limbs leapt lightly to the floor as lovely as a wave. She walked slowly away from me without so much as looking back over her shoulder; she had another purpose in her mind; and as she so gracefully and so majestically neared the door which she was seeking, a short, unpleasant man standing at the bar said, 'Puss, Puss, Puss!' and stooped to scratch her gently behind the ear. With what a wealth of singular affection, pure and profound, did she not gaze up at him, and then rub herself against his leg in token and external expression of a sacramental friendship that should never die.

This is Sylvia

by SANDY WILSON

I HAVE often been urged to write my memoirs. 'Sylvia,' my friends would say, 'of all the cats we know, yours has been the most eventful career. You have lived your nine lives to the full. Why not give your story to the public?'

But I hesitated. For I have, in the course of my adventures, been involved with many famous cats, some of whom might not relish the thought of their associations with me being related in print. There was, for instance, my first husband, who is a member of one of England's oldest aristocratic families. Our marriage and subsequent divorce caused an upheaval in London society which some people might consider best forgotten. Then there was the famous Hollywood star who was my rival, not only on celluloid but in private life as well. And in more recent years my name has been associated with various political figures who still hold positions of prominence in the Government – in fact, in one case, it was I who, believe it or not, was largely responsible for securing that position. But that was, and must remain, a close secret.

So, as I have said, I hesitated to commit my story to paper until just recently, when I had a long conversation with my friend and mentor (or should I say mentrix?), Hester Briggs, who has so often guided me in my career. I will not repeat it in full, but it ended with her saying to me:

'Sylvia, my love, you have settled down at last. You are comfortably married, and your children are well cared for. Now, while you have the leisure and before you start forgetting things, why don't you write your memoirs?

Everyone is waiting for them, and if they cause repercussions, you've got nothing to fear. Your position is secure. Go ahead, do it – if only to please your old friend Hester, who gave you a start in the world when you were a mere kitten.'

Such an appeal could hardly be disregarded. So I have finally taken the plunge, and here, for all to read and make of them what they will, are my memoirs.

*

My mother was, I should say, the most beautiful cat of her day. And she was, unlike myself, of a pure Persian strain. In fact her great-grandfather was a Sultan, whose daughter, my great-grandmother, contracted a marriage with an Anglo-Persian aristocrat whom she met while he was on a mouse-hunting expedition in Persia. He took her home to his estate just outside Catford, and there she bore him several families. The portrait of my great-grandparents surrounded by some of their children is one of the most famous paintings in the cat world. My grandmother was possessed of extraordinary good looks. She was in due course married to the eldest son of a neighbouring family, Lord Herrington of Hakeworth, her wedding being the main social event of the year; and just nine weeks later she gave birth to five kittens, three girls and two boys, the last to appear being my mother, who was christened Yasmin, after my celebrated great-grandmother.

It was of course intended that my mother should also marry a pure Persian and thus help to perpetuate the family strain. But, to my grandparents' regret, she became involved with a set which was known in its day as the Bright Young Cats. My mother had always been of an artistic frame of mind – she went in for water-colours while at school – and this inclined her towards the more Bohemian circles of Society. I never discussed this period much with her – in fact she and I very rarely discussed anything; but she would occasionally drop hints about wild parties at which cream flowed like water, which indicates that she had wandered rather far from the staid environs of her family at Hakeworth.

I must confess that in my youth, when I first discovered that my Persian strain was not as strong as it might have been, I was inclined to resent the indiscretion that had caused Mother to become involved with my father, who must, I am forced to conclude, have been a perfectly ordinary tabby with a dash of ginger. But Hester Briggs, to whom, as I have already said, I owe so much, was quick to correct my mistaken attitude.

'You should be thankful,' she told me one day, when I was feeling particularly depressed about my origins. 'Half-breeds always have the best of both worlds. Look at the Empress J— who was half black and half white. She rose to heights which a mere pure white cat would never have attained. You are destined for great things, Sylvia. If your mother had lived the life her parents wanted her to, you would now be a dull country cat with nothing to look forward to but endless families of kittens. But as it is, I'm perfectly certain you're going to have a career such as it is given to few cats to enjoy.'

How right she was!

My mother's marriage, as my grandparents prophesied, did not last. My father, whom I scarcely knew, had, as I have said, a streak of ginger – a colour which usually stands in the cat world for a roving disposition, among other things. I am not even sure what profession, if any, my father followed, my only clue being a tattered handbill which I found amongst Mother's possessions. If her husband was indeed an actor, then it explains my natural aptitude for the drama. Mother, as far as I know, never appeared on the stage, though I believe she was often called upon to sing at the parties I mentioned in the previous chapter, her special party piece being a rendition of 'Three Little Fishes' accompanied by herself on the banjo, which always went down very well. I can also remember her singing me to sleep with a popular song of my childhood, 'I'm Dreaming of a Whiting Dinner', and her voice, though small, was very sweet.

But that is a memory of my childhood. As I approached my teens, Mother became less and less in evidence and I was usually left to my own devices. I believe it was intended that I should go to Rodine College for Girl Cats, but somehow funds were never sufficient; and as Mother never bothered to keep in touch with her parents at Hakeworth, they were disinclined to pay out good money for a granddaughter they never saw.

It was at this point that Hester Briggs came into the picture. Dear Hester, what a friend she has been to me! I shall never forget that afternoon when she rang the doorbell of our tiny flat in Pimlico and discovered me in tears over a piece of cod which I was trying to prepare for supper, Mother having gone out to an afternoon crab-and-cream party in Chelsea. It turned out that Hester had been a great friend of Mother's in her youth, but had gone abroad during the Slump and opened a fish restaurant in Famagusta. She had only returned the previous day, having saved up enough money to retire to Dolphin Square, and Mother was the first friend she had decided to call on. She had no idea of my existence, but she told me that as soon as she set eyes on me, dishevelled as I was, my eyes red with weeping over the ruined cod, she took me to her heart. In fact she invited me there and then to have tea with her at Slater's, and before long I was seeing her every day and incidentally beginning to receive from her an education which I am sure has been far more useful to me than anything I could have learned at Rodine.

Hester Briggs must have been extremely pretty in her younger days. Indeed she was a central figure in the period of the Bright Young Cats, and when she finally attained her ambition by opening her own drinking and dancing establishment, the Kitty-Kat Club, all Society flocked to enjoy her hospitality and hear her entertain. I remember Mother had a record of Hester singing a popular hit of the period, 'Bye, Bye, Blackbird', and I believe she would perform this song with the aid of a heavily bejewelled mechanical blackbird by Fabergé, which would hop from table to table among the customers, continually eluding her grasp. But in spite of her constant association with the rich and the noble, Hester never lost the common touch, and I think that was an important factor in our friendship. As I have already remarked, Hester would gently reprove me when I became resentful about my mixed parentage. She herself was even more of a mixture than me, having several large black patches on her back to which she would playfully draw attention from time to time.

'Mother was white as snow,' she used to tell me, 'but Father was a real black devil. Always watch out for the black toms, Sylvia. They're the worst of the lot. Some people think they're lucky. Mother did. And look how she ended up. Me and five others due in a fortnight, not a fish-bone in the house and Father off on the spree with the little tabby next door.'

Yes, Hester had to work her way up from lowly beginnings. And all the benefits of her hard-won experience she freely showered on me. It was not long before I began to turn to her instead of to Mother for advice and help; and when Mother finally went out of my life, it seemed only natural that I should accept Hester's invitation to go and live with her in her cosy flat in Dolphin Square.

The last I was to see of Mother for some time to come was her posing for press cameras on the rail of the liner which took her to the United States. With her was Cyrus T. Rocksalmonfeller (in spite of his name, he was only half Persian, if that), owner of the vast Rocksalmonfeller Whiting Canneries in San Francisco. He and Mother had become great friends, and the idea was that I should follow her to San Francisco when she had established herself there. But I somehow knew it would be a long time before I would see Mother again. And when we did finally meet once more, how different were the circumstances from anything I could have imagined on that windy day at Southampton!

'Listen, my love,' said Hester to me at supper one night

a few weeks after Mother's departure, 'I'm afraid we must start facing facts. Much as it pains me to tell you, I don't think we shall be hearing from your Mama for some time – if ever.'

My heart sank. I was still cherishing the hope that one day soon I would follow Mother over the Atlantic and rejoin her in the Rocksalmonfeller Mansion in San Francisco. But Hester's words made me admit to myself that I had been building castles in the air. We had not even received a postcard to tell us of Mother's safe arrival, and as she had left no address, I realized I would have to resign myself to being, temporarily at any rate, an orphan.

'Now don't look so sad, ducky,' went on Hester. 'You've got me to look after you. All you've got to do now is to decide on a career. What about going on the stage?'

The stage! The idea appealed to me immediately. I knew next to nothing about the Theatre, my only personal contact with it being rather dim memories of some of Mother's friends. But I had been to several shows with Hester since she had taken me under her wing, and the bright lights and the glamour had made an indelible impression on my adolescent mind. I told Hester that I would love to be an actress, but had no idea how to go about it.

'Leave it to me,' said Hester, resourceful as always. 'I have contacts. Just drink up your milk and then off to byebyes. We want you looking your best in the morning.'

So it came about that a few weeks later I set off for my first class at Madame Alicia Whiskeronova's Academy of Drama and Dance in Notting Hill Gate. Madame Alicia was an old friend of Hester's, and she had agreed to take me on special terms, on Hester's assurance that I was extremely talented and would be a credit to Madame's Academy. Needless to say it was Hester who paid my fees, partly out of her savings and partly from the proceeds of a small gambling club which she had opened in her Dolphin Square flat on Wednesday and Saturday evenings. This I only discovered at a later date, as I was always sent off to bed early on these occasions, and was usually too exhausted after my day's classes to pay any attention to the noises that emanated from Hester's sitting-room. I believe that the police called one night, but discovered nothing, as Hester had things so carefully organized that it was a matter of minutes to dispose of the gambling apparatus and transform the gathering into what was, to all intents and purposes, a poetry-reading group, with Hester declaiming a passage from 'Old Possum'.

I have vivid recollections of my time with Madame Alicia and her sister, Madame Lydia, as indeed must many of our present-day stars who passed through their firm but loving hands. How strict Madame Alicia could be and how in awe of her we all were! Madame Lydia was gentler, but no less insistent on discipline at all times – one of the cardinal rules of the theatre. Their Academy was housed in an old drill hall which was only warmed in the winter by one unreliable oil stove; and there we would assemble, shivering with cold and nerves, for our dancing class at nine o'clock every morning. Unpunctuality was an unforgivable sin and I can remember the fearful tirade which Madame Alicia inflicted on one of my fellow-pupils, a pretty little tabby who had missed her train from Rickmansworth and arrived twenty minutes late. She was reduced to tears in no time, and her name was Lucy Trembath, who was destined to capture the heart of London when she sang 'Just My Tom' in *Pussy, Be Good.*

I must confess that I was also a victim of Madame Alicia's displeasure from time to time. I am not by nature industrious – probably because of my aristocratic lineage – and I frequently found the long hours of instruction irksome. I was particularly backward in my ballet – in fact I never did learn to do an *entrechat* – and I was sometimes guilty of slacking, whenever I could evade Madame's watchful eye and find myself a place at the back of the class. Here I was usually joined by a black-and-white tom whose name was Sylvester. He showed even less aptitude for dancing than I did, and I remember his confiding in me that he intended becoming a comedian and going to Hollywood. Both these ambitions were of course realized, and I have to smile when I recall his rendering of Othello in our end-of-term show. His playing of the murder scene gave us a distinct foretaste of his great success as the would-be assassin of Tweety-Pie, the canary.

With Madame Lydia, who acted as the voice coach, my relations were a good deal more amicable. She told me early on in my course that my singing voice, if properly trained, while it would never be of operatic proportions, would serve me very well for musical comedy. I accordingly determined to make stardom on the lighter stage my goal, a decision to which Hester gave her full backing.

'That's the way to get a rich husband,' she told me. 'The drama is all very well, but you don't hear of straight actresses marrying into the peerage, now do you?'

As a matter of fact marriage, whether or not with a peer, was the last thing I had in mind at the time. I was altogether absorbed in my theatrical career, as were all Madame's pupils. Oh, what long sessions we would have over hot milk and fried fish in Joe Lion's Café at Notting Hill Gate, discussing shows and stars and airing our views about the Theatre! We all had our favourites, whose careers we would follow with avidity. I remember Lucy Trembath, who fancied herself as a Shakespearean actress at the time, used to go in the gallery every Saturday night to watch Michael Redtail in *Hamlet* at the Mew Theatre. She always managed to get in the front row, and once nearly fell into the dress circle from excitement because, so she assured us, he waggled his whiskers at her during 'Oh, what a rogue and peasant slave am I'.

My own particular hero was Vincent Crabbe, who was then appearing in *The Dancing Toms*. I went to see the show countless times, sometimes with Hester, but more often on my own as I found a companion distracted me from my absorption in the performance. One night, in fear and trembling, I waited at the stage door to see Vincent Crabbe leaving the theatre. There was a crowd of fans there, and I only expected to have a brief glimpse of him. When he did finally emerge, he was immediately surrounded, and I hovered on the outskirts vainly hoping I might get near enough to ask him to sign my programme. To my surprise he noticed me and said laughingly, 'Who is the little lady in grey?' I was quite overwhelmed and blushed to the roots of my fur. Then I summoned up my courage and told him my name. He was absolutely charming, and signed my programme 'To Sylvia'. I think it was at that moment that I decided that, whatever else I might do, my ultimate ambition would be to play the lead in a musical comedy opposite Vincent Crabbe.

Of course, like all students, we were usually short of funds, and to remedy this we would take on all sorts of odd jobs during our holidays. Modelling, whether for artists or photographers, was the most popular choice, and Lucy Trembath told me she was able to dress herself and pay her fares out of what she made posing for Christmas and birthday cards. But then of course she was and still is a typical picture-postcard cat. Another fellow-student, a handsome black tom, whose name I forget, made quite a reputation for himself as the mascot of a well-known brand of cigarette. In fact his publicity reached such proportions that Madame Alicia told him he must choose between learning to be an actor and being, as she contemptuously called it, a 'pin-up tom'.

On Hester's advice, I decided to try my luck as a fashion model. My figure had by this time the required proportions and my looks, so I flattered myself, had the necessary touch of breeding and elegance. I began by modelling hats for that well-known fashion magazine, *Chatte*, and was told that I could make a name for myself as a mannequin, if I chose. But my ambitions lay much higher, and although I was able to make quite a lot of 'pin-money' in the photographer's studio, I only ever regarded modelling as a side-line. I don't believe it is generally known that I was the original Cuti-Cup Cat; in fact my first husband, on learning of it, endeavoured to suppress all the photographic evidence and even bought the original plates from the Cuti-Cup people and had them destroyed. I know that among certain circles that sort of thing is considered *infra dig*, but I see no reason to conceal such amusing fragments of the past from my public.

When my time with Madame Alicia was nearing its end, Hester began to busy herself with securing me some sort of professional engagement.

'You must be prepared,' she told me at the time, 'to start at the bottom. We all do it. But there's no reason why, with your looks and talent, you shouldn't work your way up to the top in no time at all.'

I feel at this point that my readers may consider themselves cheated if I do not embark on a description of struggles and heartbreak – endless auditions, culminating in the customary 'We'll let you know', jobs in the chorus of 'tatty' touring musicals, or long weeks of repertory in some grim Northern town. The truth is, though I hesitate to admit it, that I was spared all this. Within a week or so of leaving Madame Whiskeronova's I was rehearsing as a dancer in a West End revue, *Tails Up!* Needless to say, I owed this 'lucky break' mainly to Hester. For Emile Tiddler, who presented the show, had been a regular customer at the Kitty-Kat in the old days, and was only too glad to do Hester a favour by employing me. Naturally I was thrilled to bits to be working as a professional, and so was Lucy Trembath who was in the show with me, in the same dressing-room, and had managed to secure a 'spot' in the show in the big 'Pussy's Daydreams' number, in which she was to do a toe-dance dressed as a jug of cream. She had quite got over her Shakespearean phase by now, and was, like myself, set upon a career on the musical stage. We were friendly rivals – although at the time more friends than rivals. In fact we collaborated in one or two rather disgraceful practical jokes during the run of the show, which nearly earned us our dismissal from Mr Tiddler. The one I remember most vividly was perpetrated while Lucy and I were waiting to go on for the chorus number in the second half, 'Whose Kitten Are You?'. The previous number was a song *scena* which took place in a gigantic bird-cage. Two of the show-cats were standing at the back dressed as birds of paradise and Lucy and I crept behind the scenery and with great care reached up and tied their tails together. When the scene ended they both began to dash offstage to make their next change (revue is *so* exhausting) and fell flat on their faces. Lucy and I were in paroxysms – how cruel the young can be! – and nearly missed our entrance. I don't believe the two show-cats ever found out who was responsible, and I shall take this opportunity of apologizing to them at long last.

Tails Up! was moderately successful and ran for about six months. Towards the end of the run I read in *The Stage* that Vincent Crabbe was going to appear in another musical show in the autumn, for which auditions were being held at the Felix. I had always regarded that famous theatre, erected in honour of one of our greatest artists, as my Mecca, and I was a mass of nerves when I arrived, with hundreds of others, on the appointed morning, Hester's last words ringing in my ears: 'Take a deep breath before you start, and use the *whole* stage'. The Felix is of course one of the largest theatres in London, and the picture of myself attempting to use the whole of that vast stage was not an encouraging one. However, when my name was finally called, I tripped on with what was, I hope, an air of confidence, and after handing my music to the pianist launched into a verse and two choruses of 'Whose Kitten Are You?', the second chorus being taken up with as elaborate a dance routine as Hester and I could devise. To my amazement, when I had finished, applause broke out in the stalls, and I heard a voice – Vincent Crabbe's voice – say from out of the darkness, 'Thank you *very* much, Miss Sylvia'. I know that one is accustomed to hear that at the end of even the worst audition; but there was something in his tone that made me feel that he meant it. I often wonder whether he recognized me as 'the little lady in grey' to whom he had given his autograph. I don't suppose he did; but, what was more important, a day or two later I was informed that Mr

Crabbe would like me to be in his show and I was to be one of the girls' octet in the first act.

Hester and I were beside ourselves with delight.

'This calls for a celebration, my pet,' said Hester. 'Come along. Get yourself dressed up and we'll go to Prunier's.'

I protested about the expense; but Hester would have none of it.

'I've been doing rather well lately,' she said – by this time I knew about the gambling club. 'Some of the boys have been a bit reckless.'

So off we went and had a wonderful evening. I ate my first lobster and adored it.

'That's right, love,' said Hester. 'It's time you developed expensive tastes.' And I'm afraid I've followed her advice ever since.

We returned home at midnight, tired but happy, and a few days later I began rehearsing in my first show with Vincent Crabbe.

Lillian

by DAMON RUNYON

WHAT I always say is that Wilbur Willard is nothing but a very lucky guy, because what is it but luck that has him teetering along Forty-ninth Street one cold snowy morning when Lillian is mer-owing around the sidewalk looking for her mamma?

And what is it but luck that has Wilbur Willard all mulled up to a million, what with him having been sitting out a few glasses of Scotch with a friend by the name of Haggerty in an apartment over in Fifty-ninth Street? Because if Wilbur Willard is not mulled up he will see Lillian is nothing but a little black cat, and give her plenty of room, for everybody knows that black cats are terribly bad luck, even when they are only kittens.

But being mulled up like I tell you, things look very different to Wilbur Willard, and he does not see Lillian as a little black kitten scrabbling around in the snow. He sees a beautiful leopard; because a copper by the name of O'Hara, who is walking past about then, and who knows Wilbur Willard, hears him say:

'Oh, you beautiful leopard!'

The copper takes a quick peek himself, because he does not wish any leopards running around his beat, it being against the law, but all he sees, as he tells me afterwards, is this rumpot ham, Wilbur Willard, picking up a scrawny little black kitten and shoving it in his overcoat pocket, and he also hears Wilbur say:

'Your name is Lillian.'

Then Wilbur teeters on up to his room on the top floor of an old fleabag in Eighth Avenue that is called the Hotel de Brussels, where he lives quite a while, because the management does not mind actors, the management of the Hotel de Brussels being very broadminded, indeed.

There is some complaint this same morning from one of Wilbur's neighbours, an old burlesque doll by the name of Minnie Madigan, who is not working since Abraham Lincoln is assassinated, because she hears Wilbur going on in his room about a beautiful leopard, and calls up the clerk to say that a hotel which allows wild animals is not respectable. But the clerk looks in on Wilbur and finds him playing with nothing but a harmless-looking little black kitten, and nothing comes of the old doll's grouse, especially as nobody ever claims the Hotel de Brussels is respectable anyway, or at least not much.

Of course when Wilbur comes out from under the ether next afternoon he can see Lillian is not a leopard, and in fact Wilbur is quite astonished to find himself in bed with a little black kitten, because it seems Lillian is sleeping on Wilbur's chest to keep warm. At first Wilbur does not believe what he sees, and puts it down to Haggerty's Scotch, but finally he is convinced, and so he puts Lillian in his pocket, and takes her over to the Hot Box night club and gives her some milk, of which it seems Lillian is very fond.

Now where Lillian comes from in the first place of course nobody knows. The chances are somebody chucks her out of a window into the snow, because people are always chucking kittens, and one thing and another, out of windows in New York. In fact, if there is one thing this town has plenty of, it is kittens, which finally grow up to be cats, and go snooping around ash cans, and mer-owing on roofs, and keeping people from sleeping well.

Personally, I have no use for cats, including kittens, because I never seen one that has any too much sense, although I know a guy by the name of Pussy McGuire who makes a first-rate living doing nothing but stealing cats, and sometimes dogs, and selling them to old dolls who like such things for company. But Pussy only steals Persian and Angora cats, which are very fine cats, and of course Lillian is no such cat as this. Lillian is nothing but a black cat, and nobody will give you a dime a dozen for black cats in this town, as they are generally regarded as very bad jinxes.

Furthermore, it comes out in a few weeks that Wilbur Willard can just as well name her Herman, or Sidney, as not, but Wilbur sticks to Lillian, because this is the name of his partner when he is in vaudeville years ago. He often tells me about Lillian Withington when he is mulled up, which is more often than somewhat, for Wilbur is a great hand for drinking Scotch, or rye, or bourbon, or gin, or whatever else there is around for drinking, except water. In fact, Wilbur Willard is a high-class drinking man, and it does no good telling him it is against the law to drink in this country, because it only makes him mad, and he says to the dickens with the law, only Wilbur Willard uses a much rougher word than dickens.

'She is like a beautiful leopard,' Wilbur says to me about Lillian Withington. 'Black-haired, and black-eyed, and all ripply, like a leopard I see in an animal act on the same bill at the Palace with us once. We are headliners then,' he says, 'Willard and Withington, the best singing and dancing act in the country.

'I pick her up in San Antonio, which is a spot in Texas,' Wilbur says. 'She is not long out of a convent, and I just lose my old partner, Mary McGee, who ups and dies on me of pneumonia down there. Lillian wishes to go on the stage, and joins out with me. A natural-born actress with a great voice. But like a leopard,' Wilbur says. 'Like a leopard. There is cat in her, no doubt of this, and cats and women are both ungrateful. I love Lillian Withington. I wish to marry her. But she is cold to me. She says she is not going to follow the stage all her life. She says she wishes money, and luxury, and a fine home, and of course a guy like me cannot give a doll such things.

'I wait on her hand and foot,' Wilbur says. 'I am her slave. There is nothing I will not do for her. Then one day she walks in on me in Boston very cool and says she is quitting me. She says she is marrying a rich guy there. Well, naturally it busts up the act and I never have the heart to look for another partner, and then I get to belting that old black bottle around, and now what am I but a cabaret performer?'

Then sometimes he will bust out crying, and sometimes I will cry with him, although the way I look at it, Wilbur gets a pretty fair break, at that, in getting rid of a doll who wishes things he cannot give her. Many a guy in this town is tangled up with a doll who wishes things he cannot give her, but who keeps him tangled up just the same and busting himself trying to keep her quiet.

Wilbur makes pretty fair money as an entertainer in the Hot Box, though he spends most of it for Scotch, and he is not a bad entertainer, either. I often go to the Hot Box when I am feeling blue to hear him sing *Melancholy Baby*, and *Moonshine Valley*, and other sad songs which break my heart. Personally, I do not see why any doll cannot love Wilbur, especially if they listen to him sing such songs as *Melancholy Baby* when he is mulled up well, because he is a tall, nice-looking guy with long eyelashes, and sleepy brown eyes, and his voice has a low moaning sound that usually goes very big with the dolls. In fact, many a doll does do some pitching to Wilbur when he is singing in the Hot Box, but somehow Wilbur never gives them a tumble, which I suppose is because he is thinking only of Lillian Withington.

Well, after he gets Lillian, the black kitten, Wilbur seems to find a new interest in life, and Lillian turns out to be right cute, and not bad-looking after Wilbur gets her fed up well. She is blacker than a yard up a chimney, with not a white spot on her, and she grows so fat that by and by Wilbur cannot carry her in his pocket any more, so he puts a collar on her and leads her around. So Lillian becomes very well known on Broadway, what with Wilbur taking her to many places, and finally she does not even have to be led around by Willard, but follows him like a pooch. And in all the Roaring Forties there is no pooch that cares to have any truck with Lillian, for she will leap aboard them quicker than you can say scat, and scratch and bite them until they are very glad indeed to get away from her.

But of course the pooches in the Forties are mainly nothing but Chows, and Pekes, and Poms, or little woolly white poodles, which are led around by blonde dolls, and are not fit to take their own part against a smart cat. In fact, Wilbur Willard is finally not on speaking terms with any doll that owns a pooch between Times Square and Columbus Circle, and they are all hoping that both Wilbur and Lillian will go lay down and die somewhere. Furthermore, Wilbur has a couple of battles with guys who also belong to the dolls, but Wilbur is no boob in a battle if he is not mulled up too much and leg-weary.

After he is through entertaining people in the Hot Box, Wilbur generally goes around to any speakeasies which may still be open, and does a little off-hand drinking on top of what he already drinks down in the Hot Box, which is plenty, and although it is considered very risky in this town to mix Hot Box liquor with any other, it never seems to bother Wilbur. Along toward daylight he takes a couple of bottles of Scotch over to his room in the Hotel de Brussels and uses them for a nightcap, so by the time Wilbur Willard is ready to slide off to sleep he has plenty of liquor of one kind and another inside him, and he sleeps pretty good.

Of course nobody on Broadway blames Wilbur so very much for being such a rumpot, because they know about him loving Lillian Withington and losing her, and it is considered a reasonable excuse in this town for a guy to do some drinking when he loses a doll, which is why there is so much drinking here, but it is a mystery to one and all how Wilbur stands all this liquor without croaking. The cemeteries are full of guys who do a lot less drinking than Wilbur, but he never even seems to feel extra tough, or if he does he keeps it to himself and does not go around saying it is the kind of liquor you get nowadays.

He costs some of the boys around Mindy's plenty of dough one winter, because he starts in doing most of his drinking after hours in Good Time Charley's speakeasy, and the boys lay a price of four to one against him lasting until spring, never figuring a guy can drink very much of Good Time Charley's liquor and keep on living. But Wilbur Willard does it just the same, so everybody says the guy is just naturally superhuman, and lets it go at that.

Sometimes Wilbur drops into Mindy's with Lillian following him on the look-out for pooches, or riding on his shoulder if the weather is bad, and the two of them will sit with us for hours chewing the rag about one thing and another. At such times Wilbur generally has a bottle on his hip and takes a shot now and then, but of course this does not come under the head of serious drinking with him. When Lillian is with Wilbur she always lies as close to him as she can get and anybody can see that she seems to be very fond of Wilbur, and that he is very fond of her, although he sometimes forgets himself and speaks of her as a beautiful leopard. But of course this is only a slip of the tongue, and anyway if Wilbur gets any pleasure out of thinking Lillian is a leopard, it is nobody's business but his own.

'I suppose she will run away from me some day,' Wilbur says, running his hand over Lillian's back until her fur crackles. 'Yes, although I give her plenty of liver and catnip, and one thing and another, and all my affection, she will probably give me the go-by. Cats are like women, and women are like cats. They are both very ungrateful.'

'They are both generally bad luck,' Big Nig, the crap shooter says. 'Especially cats, and most especially black cats.'

Many other guys tell Wilbur about black cats being bad luck, and advise him to slip Lillian into the North River some night with a sinker on her, but Wilbur claims he already has all the bad luck in the world when he loses Lillian Withington, and that Lillian, the cat, cannot make it any worse, so he goes on taking extra good care of her, and Lillian goes on getting bigger and bigger until I commence thinking maybe there is some St Bernard in her.

Finally I commence to notice something funny about

Lillian. Sometimes she will be acting very loving towards Wilbur, and then again she will be very unfriendly to him, and will spit at him, and snatch at him with her claws, very hostile. It seems to me that she is all right when Wilbur is mulled up, but is as sad and fretful as he is himself when he is only a little bit mulled. And when Lillian is sad and fretful she makes it very tough indeed on the pooches in the neighbourhood of the Brussels.

In fact, Lillian takes to pooch-hunting, sneaking off when Wilbur is getting his rest, and running pooches bow-legged, especially when she finds one that is not on a leash. A loose pooch is just naturally cherry pie for Lillian.

Well, of course this causes great indignation among the dolls who own the pooches, particularly when Lillian comes home one day carrying a Peke as big as she is herself by the scruff of the neck, and with a very excited blonde doll following her and yelling bloody murder outside Wilbur Willard's door when Lillian pops into Wilbur's room through a hole he cuts in the door for her, still lugging the Peke. But it seems that instead of being mad at Lillian and giving her a pasting for such goings on, Wilbur is somewhat pleased, because he happens to be still in a fog when Lillian arrives with the Peke, and is thinking of Lillian as a beautiful leopard.

'Why,' Wilbur says, 'this is devotion, indeed. My beautiful leopard goes off into the jungle and fetches me an antelope for dinner.'

Now of course there is no sense whatever to this, because a Peke is certainly not anything like an antelope, but the blonde doll outside Wilbur's door hears Wilbur mumble, and gets the idea that he is going to eat her Peke for dinner and the squawk she puts up is very terrible. There is plenty of trouble around the Brussels in cooling the blonde doll's rage over Lillian snagging her Peke, and what is more the blonde doll's ever loving guy, who turns out to be a tough Ginney bootlegger by the name of Gregorio, shows up at the Hot Box the next night and wishes to put the slug on Wilbur Willard.

But Wilbur rounds him up with a few drinks and by singing *Melancholy Baby* to him, and before he leaves the Ginney gets very sentimental towards Wilbur, and Lillian, too, and wishes to give Wilbur five bucks to let Lillian grab the Peke again, if Lillian will promise not to bring it back. It seems Gregorio does not really care for the Peke, and is only acting quarrelsome to please the blonde doll and make her think he loves her dearly.

But I can see Lillian is having different moods, and finally I ask Wilbur if he notices it.

'Yes,' he says, very sad, 'I do not seem to be holding her love. She is getting very fickle. A guy moves on to my floor at the Brussels the other day with a little boy, and Lillian becomes very fond of this kid at once. In fact, they are great friends. Ah, well,' Wilbur says, 'cats are like women. Their affection does not last.'

I happen to go over to the Brussels a few days later to explain to a guy by the name of Crutchy, who lives on the same floor as Wilbur Willard, that some of our citizens do not like his face and that it may be a good idea for him to leave town, especially if he insists on bringing ale into their territory, and I see Lillian out in the hall with a youngster which I judge is the kid Wilbur is talking about. This kid is maybe three years old, and very cute, what with black hair and black eyes, and he is mauling Lillian around the hall in a way that is most surprising, for Lillian is not such a cat as will stand for much mauling around, not even from Wilbur Willard.

I am wondering how anybody comes to take such a kid to a place like the Brussels, but I figure it is some actor's kid, and that maybe there is no mamma for it. Later I am talking to Wilbur about this, and he says:

'Well, if the kid's old man is an actor, he is not working at it. He sticks close to his room all the time, and he does not allow the kid to go anywhere but in the hall, and I feel sorry for the little guy, which is why I allow Lillian to play with him.'

Now it comes on a very cold spell, and a bunch of us are

sitting in Mindy's along towards five o'clock in the morning when we hear fire engines going past. By and by in comes a guy by the name of Kansas, who is named Kansas because he comes from Kansas, and who is a gambler by trade.

'The old Brussels is on fire,' this guy Kansas says.

'She is always on fire,' Big Nig says, meaning there is always plenty of hot stuff going on around the Brussels.

About this time who walks in but Wilbur Willard, and anybody can see he is just naturally floating. The chances are he comes from Good Time Charley's, and is certainly carrying plenty of pressure. I never see Wilbur Willard mulled up more. He does not have Lillian with him, but then he never takes Lillian to Good Time Charley's because Charley hates cats.

'Hey, Wilbur,' Big Nig says, 'your joint, the Brussels, is on fire.'

'Well,' Wilbur says, 'I am a little firefly, and I need a light. Let us go where there is a fire.'

The Brussels is only a few blocks from Mindy's and there is nothing else to do just then, so some of us walk over to Eighth Avenue with Wilbur teetering along ahead of us. The old shack is certainly roaring away when we get in sight of it, and the firemen are tossing water into it, and the coppers have the fire lines out to keep the crowd back, although there is not much of a crowd at such an hour in the morning.

'Is it not beautiful?' Wilbur Willard says, looking up at the flames. 'Is it not like a fairy palace all lighted up this way?'

You see, Wilbur does not realize the place is on fire, although guys and dolls are running out of it every which way, most of them half dressed, or not dressed at all, and the firemen are getting out the life nets in case anybody wishes to hop out of the window.

'It is certainly beautiful,' Wilbur says, 'I must get Lillian so she can see this.'

And before anybody has time to think, there is Wilbur Willard walking into the front door of the Brussels as if nothing happens. The firemen and the coppers are so astonished all they can do is holler at Wilbur, but he pays no attention whatever. Well, naturally everybody figures Wilbur is a gone gosling, but in about ten minutes he comes walking out of this same door through the fire and smoke as cool as you please, and he has Lillian in his arms.

'You know,' Wilbur says, coming over to where we are standing with our eyes popping out, 'I have to walk all the way up to my floor because the elevators seem to be out of commission. The service is getting terrible in this hotel. I will certainly make a strong complaint to the management about it as soon as I pay something on my account.'

Then what happens but Lillian lets out a big mer-row, and hops out of Wilbur's arms and skips past the coppers and the firemen with her back all humped up, and the next thing anybody knows she is tearing through the front door of the old hotel and making plenty of speed.

'Well, well,' Wilbur says, looking much surprised, 'there goes Lillian.'

And what does this daffy Wilbur Willard do but turn and go marching back into the Brussels again, and by this time the smoke is pouring out of the front doors so thick he is out of sight in a second. Naturally he takes the coppers and firemen by surprise, because they are not used to guys walking in and out of fires on them.

This time anybody standing around will lay you plenty of odds – two and a half and maybe three to one – that Wilbur never shows up again, because the old Brussels is now just popping with fire and smoke from the lower windows, although there does not seem to be quite so much fire in the upper storey. Everybody seems to be out of the building, and even the firemen are fighting the blaze from the outside because the Brussels is so old and ramshackly there is no sense in them risking the floors.

I mean everybody is out of the place except Wilbur Willard and Lillian, and we figure they are getting a good frying somewhere inside, although Feet Samuels is around offering to take thirteen to five for a few small bets that

Lillian comes out okay, because Feet claims that a cat has nine lives and that is a fair bet at the price.

Well, up comes a swell-looking doll all heated up about something and pushing and clawing her way through the crowd up to the ropes and screaming until you can hardly hear yourself think, and about this same minute everybody hears a voice going ai-lee-hi-hee-hoo, like a Swiss yodeller, which comes from the roof of the Brussels, and looking up what do we see but Wilbur Willard standing up there on the edge of the roof, high above the fire and smoke, and yodelling very loud.

Under one arm he has a big bundle of some kind, and under the other he has the little kid I see playing in the hall with Lillian. As he stands up there going ai-lee-hi-hee-hoo, the swell-dressed doll near us begins screaming louder than Wilbur is yodelling, and the firemen rush over under him with a life net.

Wilbur lets go another ai-lee-hee-hoo, and down he comes all spraddled out, with the bundle and the kid, but he hits the net sitting down and bounces up and back again for a couple of minutes before he finally settles. In fact, Wilbur is enjoying the bouncing, and the chances are he will be bouncing yet if the firemen do not drop their hold on the net and let him fall to the ground.

Then Wilbur steps out of the net, and I can see the bundle is a rolled-up blanket with Lillian's eyes peeking out of one end. He still has the kid under the other arm with his head stuck out in front, and his legs stuck out behind, and it does not seem to me that Wilbur is handling the kid as careful as he is handling Lillian. He stands there looking at the firemen with a very sneering look, and finally he says:

'Do not think you can catch me in your net unless I wish to be caught. I am a butterfly, and very hard to overtake.'

Then all of a sudden the swell-dressed doll who is doing so much hollering, piles on top of Wilbur and grabs the kid from him and begins hugging and kissing it.

'Wilbur,' she says, 'God bless you, Wilbur, for saving my baby! Oh, thank you, Wilbur, thank you! My wretched husband kidnaps and runs away with him, and it is only a few hours ago that my detectives find out where he is.'

Wilbur gives the doll a funny look for about half a minute and starts to walk away, but Lillian comes wiggling out of the blanket, looking and smelling pretty much singed up, and the kid sees Lillian and begins hollering for her, so Wilbur finally hands Lillian over to the kid. And not wishing to leave Lillian, Wilbur stands around somewhat confused, and the doll gets talking to him, and finally they go away together, and as they go Wilbur is carrying the kid, and the kid is carrying Lillian, and Lillian is not feeling so good from her burns.

Furthermore, Wilbur is probably more sober than he ever is before in years at this hour in the morning, but before they go I get a chance to talk some to Wilbur when he is still rambling somewhat, and I make out from what he says that the first time he goes to get Lillian he finds her in his room and does not see hide or hair of the little kid and does not even think of him, because he does not know what room the kid is in, anyway, having never noticed such a thing.

But the second time he goes up, Lillian is sniffing at the crack under the door of a room down the hall from Wilbur's and Wilbur says he seems to remember seeing a trickle of something like water coming out of the crack.

'And,' Wilbur says, 'as I am looking for a blanket for Lillian, and it will be a bother to go back to my room, I figure I will get one out of this room. I try the knob but the door is locked, so I kick it in, and walk in to find the room is full of smoke, and fire is shooting through the windows very lovely, and when I grab a blanket off the bed for Lillian, what is under the blanket but the kid?

'Well,' Wilbur says, 'the kid is squawking and Lillian is mer-owing, and there is so much confusion generally that it makes me nervous, so I figure we better go up on the roof and let the stink blow off us, and look at the fire from there. It seems there is a guy stretched out on the floor of the room alongside an upset table between the door and the bed. He has a bottle in one hand, and he is dead. Well, naturally there is nothing to be gained by lugging a dead guy along, so I take Lillian and the kid and go up on the roof, and we just naturally fly off like humming birds. Now I must get a drink,' Wilbur says. 'I wonder if anybody has anything on their hip?'

Well, the papers are certainly full of Wilbur and Lillian the next day, especially Lillian, and they are both great heroes.

But Wilbur cannot stand publicity very long, because he never has no time to himself for his drinking, what with the scribes and the photographers hopping on him every few minutes wishing to hear his story, and to take more pictures of him and Lillian, so one night he disappears, and Lillian disappears with him.

About a year later it comes out that he marries his old doll, Lillian Withington-Harmon, and falls into a lot of dough, and what is more he cuts out the liquor and becomes quite a useful citizen one way and another. So everybody has to admit that black cats are not always bad luck, although I say Wilbur's case is a little exception because he does not start out knowing Lillian is a black cat, but thinking she is a leopard.

I happen to run into Wilbur one day all dressed up in good clothes and jewellery, and cutting quite a swell.

'Wilbur,' I says to him, 'I often think how remarkable it is the way Lillian suddenly gets such an attachment for the little kid and remembers about him being in the hotel and leads you back there a second time to the right room. If I do not see this come off with my own eyes, I will never believe a cat has brains enough to do such a thing, because I consider cats are extra dumb.'

'Brains nothing,' Wilbur says. 'Lillian does not have brains enough to grease a gimlet. And what is more she has no more attachment for the kid than a jack rabbit. The time has come,' Wilbur says, 'to expose Lillian. She gets a lot of credit which is never coming to her. I will now tell you about Lillian, and nobody knows this but me.

'You see,' Wilbur says, 'when Lillian is a little kitten I always put a little Scotch in her milk, partly to help make her good and strong, and partly because I am never no hand to drink alone, unless there is nobody with me. Well, at first Lillian does not care so much for this Scotch in her milk, but finally she takes a liking to it, and I keep making her toddy stronger until in the end she will lap up a good big snort without any milk for a chaser, and yell for more. In fact, I suddenly realize that Lillian becomes a rumpot, just like I am in those days, and simply must have her grog, and it is when she is good and rummed up that Lillian goes off snatching Pekes, and acting tough generally.

'Now,' Wilbur says, 'the time of the fire is about the time I get home every morning and give Lillian her Schnapps. But when I go into the hotel and get her the first time I forget to Scotch her up, and the reason she runs back into the hotel is because she is looking for her shot. And the reason she is sniffing at the kid's door is not because the kid is in there but because the trickle that is coming through the crack under the door is nothing but Scotch running out of the bottle in the dead guy's hand. I never mention this before because I figure it may be a knock to a dead guy's memory,' Wilbur says. 'Drinking is certainly a disgusting thing, especially secret drinking.'

'But how is Lillian getting along these days?' I ask Wilbur Willard.

'I am greatly disappointed in Lillian,' he says. 'She refuses to reform when I do and the last I hear of her she takes up with Gregorio, the Ginney bootlegger, who keeps her well Scotched up all the time so she will lead his blonde doll's Peke a dog's life.'

The Fat Cat

by Q. Patrick

The marines found her when they finally captured the old mission house at Fufa. After two days of relentless pounding, they hadn't expected to find anything alive there – least of all a fat cat.

And she was a very fat cat, sandy as a Scotsman, with enormous agate eyes and a fat amiable face. She sat there on the mat – or rather what was left of the mat – in front of what had been the mission porch, licking her paws as placidly as if the shell-blasted jungle were a summer lawn in New Jersey.

One of the men, remembering his childhood primer, quoted: 'The fat cat sat on the mat'.

The other men laughed; not that the remark was really funny, but laughter broke the tension and expressed their relief at having at last reached their objective, after two days of bitter fighting.

The fat cat, still sitting on the mat, smiled at them, as if to show she didn't mind the joke being on her. Then she saw Corporal Randy Jones, and for some reason known only to herself ran towards him as though he was her long-lost master. With a refrigerator purr, she weaved in and out of his muddy legs.

Everyone laughed again as Randy picked her up and pushed his ugly face against the sleek fur. It was funny to see any living thing show a preference for the dour, solitary Randy.

A sergeant flicked his fingers. 'Kitty. Come here. We'll make you B Company mascot.'

But the cat, perched on Randy's shoulder like a queen on her throne, merely smiled down majestically as much as to say: 'You can be my subjects if you like. But this is my man – my royal consort.'

And never for a second did she swerve from her devotion. She lived with Randy, slept with him, ate only food provided by him. Almost every man in Company B tried to seduce her with caresses and morsels of canned ration, but all advances were met with a yawn of contempt.

For Randy this new love was ecstasy. He guarded her with the possessive tenderness of a mother. He combed her fur sleek; he almost starved himself to maintain her fatness. And all the time there was a strange wonder in him. The homeliest and ungainliest of ten in a West Virginia mining family, he had never before aroused affection in man or woman. No one had counted for him until the fat cat.

*

Randy's felicity, however, was short-lived. In a few days B Company was selected to carry out a flanking movement to surprise and possibly capture the enemy's headquarters, known to be twenty miles away through dense, sniper-infested jungle. The going would be rugged. Each man would carry his own supply of food and water, and sleep in foxholes with no support from the base.

The CO was definite about the fat cat: the stricken Randy was informed that the presence of a cat would seriously endanger the safety of the whole company. If it were seen following him, it would be shot on sight. Just before their scheduled departure, Randy carried the fat cat over to the mess of Company H, where she was enthusiastically received by an equally fat cook. Randy could not bring himself to look back at the reproachful stare which he knew would be in the cat's agate eyes.

But all through that first day of perilous jungle travel, the thought of the cat's stare haunted him, and he was prey to all the heartache of parting; in leaving the cat, he had left behind wife, mother, and child.

Darkness, like an immense black parachute, had descended hours ago on the jungle, when Randy was awakened from exhausted sleep. Something soft and warm was brushing his cheek; and his foxhole resounded to a symphony of purring. He stretched out an incredulous hand, but this was no dream. Real and solid, the cat was curled in a contented ball at his shoulder.

His first rush of pleasure was chilled as he remembered his CO's words. The cat, spurning the blandishments of H Company's cuisine, had followed him through miles of treacherous jungle, only to face death the moment daylight revealed her presence. Randy was in an agony of uncertainty. To carry her back to the base would be desertion. To beat and drive her away was beyond the power of his simple nature.

The cat nuzzled his face again and breathed a mournful meow. She was hungry, of course, after her desperate trek. Suddenly Randy saw what he must do. If he could bring himself not to feed her, hunger would surely drive her back to the sanctuary of the cook.

She meowed again. He shushed her and gave her a half-hearted slap. 'Aain't got nothing for you, honey. Scram. Go home. Scat.'

To his mingled pleasure and disappointment, she leaped silently out of the foxhole. When morning came there was no sign of her.

As B Company inched its furtive advance through the dense undergrowth, Randy felt the visit from the cat must have been a dream. But on the third night it came again. It brushed against his cheek and daintily took his ear in its teeth. When it meowed, the sound was still soft and cautious, but held a pitiful quaver of beseechment which cut through Randy like a Jap bayonet.

On its first visit, Randy had not seen the cat, but tonight some impulse made him reach for his flashlight. Holding it carefully downward, he turned it on. What he saw was the ultimate ordeal. The fat cat was fat no longer. Her body sagged; her sleek fur was matted and mud-stained, her paws torn and bloody. But it was the eyes, blinking up at him, that were the worst. There was no hint of reproach

in them, only an expression of infinite trust and pleading.

Forgetting everything but those eyes, Randy tugged out one of his few remaining cans of ration. At the sight of it, the cat weakly licked its lips. Randy moved to open the can. Then the realization that he would be signing the cat's death warrant surged over him. And, because the pent-up emotion in him had to have some outlet, it turned into unreasoning anger against this animal whose suffering had become more than he could bear. 'Scat,' he hissed. But the cat did not move.

He lashed out at her with the heavy flashlight. For a second she lay motionless under the blow. Then with a little moan she fled.

The next night she did not come back and Randy did not sleep.

On the fifth day they reached really dangerous territory. Randy and another marine, Joe, were sent forward to scout for the Jap command headquarters. Suddenly, weaving through the jungle, they came upon it.

A profound silence hung over the glade, with its two hastily erected shacks. Peering through the dense foliage, they saw traces of recent evacuation – waste paper scattered on the grass, a pile of fresh garbage, a Jap army shirt flapping on a tree. Outside one of the shacks, under an awning, stretched a rough table strewn with the remains of a meal. 'They must have got wind of us and scrammed,' breathed Joe.

Randy edged forward – then froze as something stirred in the long grasses near the door of the first shack. As he watched, the once fat cat hobbled out into the sunlight.

A sense of heightened danger warred with Randy's pride that she had not abandoned him. Stiff with suspense, he watched it disappear into the shack. Soon it padded out.

'No Japs,' said Joe. 'That cat'd have raised 'em sure as shooting.'

He started boldly into the glade. 'Hey, Randy, there's a

whole chicken on that table. Chicken's going to taste good after K rations.'

He broke off, for the cat had seen the chicken too, and with pitiful clumsiness had leaped on to the table. With an angry yell Joe stooped for a rock and threw it.

Indignation blazed in Randy. He'd starved and spurned the cat, and yet she'd followed him with blind devotion. The chicken, surely, should be her reward. In his slow, simple mind it seemed the most important thing in the world for his beloved to have her fair share of the booty.

The cat, seeing the rock coming, lumbered off the table, just in time, for the rock struck the chicken squarely, knocking it off its plate.

Randy leaped into the clearing. As he did so, a deafening explosion made him drop to the ground. A few seconds later, when he raised himself, there was no table, no shack, nothing but a blazing wreckage of wood.

Dazedly he heard Joe's voice: 'Booby trap under that chicken. Gee, if that cat hadn't jumped for it, I wouldn't have hurled the rock; we'd have grabbed it ourselves – and we'd be in heaven now.' His voice dropped to an awed whisper. 'That cat, I guess it's blown to hell . . . But it saved our lives.' Randy couldn't speak. There was a constriction in his throat. He lay there, feeling more desolate than he'd ever felt in his life before.

Then from behind came a contented purr.

He spun round. Freakishly, the explosion had hurled a crude rush mat out of the shack. It had come to rest on the grass behind him.

And, seated serenely on the mat, the cat was smiling at him.

Faith

(From an inscription in St Augustine's Church, Watling Street, London, E.C.)

'... On Monday, September 9th, 1940, she endured horrors and perils beyond the power of words to tell.

'Shielding her kitten in a sort of recess in the house (a spot she selected only three days before the tragedies occurred), she sat the whole frightful night of bombing and fire, guarding her little kitten.

'The roofs and masonry exploded, the whole house blazed, four floors fell through in front of her. Fire and ruin all around her.

'Yet she stayed calm and steadfast and waited for help.

'We rescued her in the early morning while the place was still burning, and by the mercy of Almighty God she and her kitten were not only saved, but unhurt...'

The White Cat

by W. W. Jacobs

The traveller stood looking from the tap room window of the *Cauliflower* at the falling rain. The village street below was empty, and everything was quiet with the exception of the garrulous old man smoking with much enjoyment on the settle behind him.

'It'll do a power o' good,' said the ancient, craning his neck round the edge of the settle and turning a bleared eye on the window. 'I ain't like some folk; I never did mind a drop o' rain.'

The traveller grunted and, returning to the settle opposite the old man, fell to lazily stroking a cat which had strolled in attracted by the warmth of the small fire which smouldered in the grate.

'He's a good mouser,' said the old man, 'but I expect that Smith the landlord would sell 'im to anybody for arf a crown; but we 'ad a cat in Claybury once that you couldn't ha' bought for a hundred golden sovereigns.'

The traveller continued to caress the cat.

'A white cat, with one yaller eye, and one blue one,' continued the old man. 'It sounds queer, but it's as true as I sit 'ere wishing that I 'ad another mug o' ale as good as the last you gave me.'

The traveller, with a start that upset the cat's nerves, finished his own mug, and then ordered both to be refilled. He stirred the fire into a blaze, and, lighting his pipe and putting one foot on to the hob, prepared to listen.

It used to belong to old man Clark, young Joe Clark's uncle, said the ancient, smacking his lips delicately over the ale and extending a tremulous claw to the tobacco pouch pushed towards him; and he was never tired of showing it off to people. He used to call it 'is blue-eyed darling, and the fuss 'e made o' that cat was sinful.

Young Joe Clark couldn't bear it, but being down in 'is uncle's will for five cottages and a bit o' land bringing in about forty pounds a year, he 'ad to 'ide his feelings and pretend as he loved it. He used to take it little drops o' cream and tit-bits o' meat, and old Clark was so pleased that 'e promised 'im that he should 'ave the cat along with all the other property when 'e was dead.

Young Joe said he couldn't thank 'im enough, and the old man, who 'ad been ailing a long time, made 'im come up every day to teach 'im 'ow to cook its meat and then chop it up fine; 'ow it liked a clean saucer every time for its milk; and 'ow he wasn't to make a noise when it was asleep.

'Take care your children don't worry it, Joe,' he sez one day, very sharp. 'One o' your boys was pulling its tail this morning, and I want you to clump his 'ead for 'im.'

'Which one was it?' sez Joe.

'The slobbery-nosed one,' says old Clark.

'I'll give 'im a clout as soon as I get 'ome,' sez Joe, who was very fond of 'is children.

'Go and fetch 'im and do it 'ere,' sez the old man; 'that'll teach 'im to love animals.'

Joe went off 'ome to fetch the boy, and arter his mother 'ad washed his face, and wiped his nose, an' put a clean pinneyfore on 'im, he took 'im to 'is uncle's and clouted his 'ead for 'im. Arter that Joe and 'is wife 'ad words all night long, and next morning old Clark, coming in from the garden, was just in time to see 'im kick the cat right acrost the kitchen.

He could 'ardly speak for a minute, and when 'e could Joe see plain wot a fool he'd been. Fust of all 'e called Joe every name he could think of – which took 'im a long time – and then he ordered 'im out of 'is house.

'You shall 'ave my money wen your betters have done with it,' he sez, 'and not afore. That's all you've done for yourself.'

Joe Clark didn't know what he meant at the time, but

when old Clark died three months arterwards 'e found out. His uncle 'ad made a new will and left everything to old George Barstow for as long as the cat lived, providing that he took care of it. When the cat was dead the property was to go to Joe.

The cat was only two years old at the time, and George Barstow, who was arf crazy with joy, said it shouldn't be 'is fault if it didn't live another twenty years.

The funny thing was the quiet way Joe Clark took it. He didn't seem to be at all cut up about it, and when Henery Walker said it was a shame, 'e said he didn't mind, and that George Barstow was a old man, and he was quite welcome to 'ave the property as long as the cat lived.

'It must come to me by the time I'm an old man,' he sez, 'and that's all I care about.'

Henery Walker went off, and as 'e passed the cottage where old Clark used to live, and which George Barstow 'ad moved into, 'e spoke to the old man over the palings and told 'im wot Joe Clark 'ad said. George Barstow only grunted and went on stooping and prying over 'is front garden.

'Bin and lost something?' sez Henery Walker, watching 'im.

'No; I'm finding,' sez George Barstow, very fierce, and picking up something. 'That's the fifth bit o' powdered liver I've found in my garden this morning.'

Henery Walker went off whistling, and the opinion he'd 'ad 'o Joe Clark began to improve. He spoke to Joe about it that arternoon, and Joe said that if 'e ever accused 'im o' such a thing again he'd knock 'is 'ead off. He said that he 'oped the cat 'ud live to be a hundred, and that 'e'd no more think of giving it poisoned meat than Henery Walker would of paying for 'is drink so long as 'e could get anybody else to do it for 'im.

They 'ad bets up at this 'ere Cauliflower public-'ouse that evening as to 'ow long that cat 'ud live. Nobody gave it more than a month, and Bill Chambers sat and thought o' so many ways o' killing it on the sly that it was wunnerful to hear 'im.

George Barstow took fright when he 'eard of them, and the care 'e took o' that cat was wunnerful to behold. Arf its time it was shut up in the back bedroom, and the other arf George Barstow was fussing arter it till that cat got to hate 'im like pison. Instead o' giving up work as he'd thought to do, 'e told Henery Walker that 'e'd never worked so hard in his life.

'Wot about fresh air and exercise for it?' sez Henery.

'Wot about Joe Clark?' sez George Barstow. 'I'm tied 'and and foot. I dursent leave the house for a moment. I ain't been to the Cauliflower since I've 'ad it, and three times I got out o' bed last night to see if it was safe.'

'Mark my words,' sez Henery Walker; 'if that cat don't 'ave exercise, you'll lose it.'

'I shall lose it if it does 'ave exercise,' sez George Barstow, 'that I know.'

He sat down thinking arter Henery Walker 'ad gone, and then he 'ad a little collar and chain made for it, and took it out for a walk. Pretty nearly every dog in Claybury went with 'em, and the cat was in such a state o' mind afore they got 'ome he couldn't do anything with it. It 'ad a fit as soon as they got indoors, and George Barstow, who 'ad read about children's fits in the almanac, gave it a warm bath. It brought it round immediate, and then it began to tear round the room and up and downstairs till George Barstow was afraid to go near it.

It was so bad that evening, sneezing, that George Barstow went for Bill Chambers, who'd got a good name for doctoring animals, and asked 'im to give it something. Bill said he'd got some powders at 'ome that would cure it at once, and he went and fetched 'em and mixed one up with a bit o' butter.

'That's the way to give a cat medicine,' he sez; 'smear it with the butter and then it'll lick it off, powder and all.'

He was just going to rub it on the cat when George Barstow caught 'old of 'is arm and stopped 'im.

'How do I know it ain't poison?' he sez. 'You're a friend

o' Joe Clark's, and for all I know he may ha' paid you to pison it.'

'I wouldn't do such a thing,' sez Bill. 'You ought to know me better than that.'

'All right,' sez George Barstow; 'you eat it then, and I'll give you two shillings instead o' one. You can easy mix some more.'

'Not me,' sez Bill Chambers, making a face.

'Well, three shillings, then,' sez George Barstow, getting more and more suspicious like; 'four shillings – five shillings.'

Bill Chambers shook his 'ead, and George Barstow, more and more certain that he 'ad caught 'im trying to kill 'is cat and that 'e wouldn't eat the stuff, rose 'im up to ten shillings.

Bill looked at the butter and then 'e looked at the ten shillings on the table, and at last he shut 'is eyes and gulped it down and put the money in 'is pocket.

'You see, I 'ave to be careful, Bill,' sez George Barstow, rather upset.

Bill Chambers didn't answer 'im. He sat there as white as a sheet, and making such extraordinary faces that George was arf afraid of 'im.

'Anything wrong, Bill?' he sez at last.

Bill sat staring at 'im, and then all of a sudden he clapped 'is 'andkerchief to 'is mouth and, getting up from his chair, opened the door and rushed out. George Barstow thought at fust that he 'ad eaten pison for the sake o' the ten shillings, but when 'e remembered that Bill Chambers 'ad got the most delikit stummock in Claybury he altered 'is mind.

The cat was better next morning, but George Barstow had 'ad such a fright about it 'e wouldn't let it go out of 'is sight, and Joe Clark began to think that 'e would 'ave to wait longer for that property than 'e had thought, arter all. To 'ear 'im talk anybody'd ha' thought that 'e loved that cat. We didn't pay much attention to it up at the Cauliflower 'ere, except maybe to wink at 'im – a thing he couldn't a-bear – but at 'ome, o' course, his young 'uns thought as everything he said was Gospel; and one day, coming 'ome from work, as he was passing George Barstow's he was paid out for his deceitfulness.

'I've wronged you, Joe Clark,' sez George Barstow, coming to the door, 'and I'm sorry for it.'

'Oh!' sez Joe staring.

'Give that to your little Jimmy,' sez George Barstow, giving 'im a shilling. 'I've give 'im one, but I thought arterwards it wasn't enough.'

'What for?' sez Joe, staring at 'im again.

'For bringing my cat 'ome,' sez George Barstow. ''Ow it got out I can't think, but I lost it for three hours, and I'd about given it up when your little Jimmy brought it to me in 'is arms. He's a fine little chap and 'e does you credit.'

Joe Clark tried to speak, but he couldn't get a word out, and Henery Walker, wot 'ad just come up and 'eard wot passed, took hold of 'is arm and helped 'im home. He walked like a man in a dream, but arf-way he stopped and cut a stick from the hedge to take 'ome to little Jimmy. He said the boy 'ad been asking him for a stick for some time, but up till then 'e'd always forgotten it.

At the end o' the fust year that cat was still alive, to everybody's surprise; but George Barstow took such care of it 'e never let it out of 'is sight. Every time 'e went out he took it with 'im in a hamper, and, to prevent its being pisoned, he paid Isaac Sawyer, who 'ad the biggest family in Claybury, sixpence a week to let one of 'is boys taste its milk before it had it.

The second year it was ill twice, but the horse-doctor that George Barstow got for it said that it was as 'ard as nails, and with care it might live to be twenty. He said that it wanted more fresh air and exercise; but when he 'eard 'ow George Barstow came by it he said that p'r'aps it would live longer indoors arter all.

At last one day, when George Barstow 'ad been living on the fat o' the land for nearly three years, that cat got out again. George 'ad raised the front room winder two or three inches to throw something outside, and, afore he knew wot was 'appening, the cat was outside and going up the road about twenty miles an hour.

George Barstow went after it, but he might as well ha' tried to catch the wind. The cat was arf wild with joy at getting out again, and he couldn't get within arf a mile of it.

He stayed out all day without food or drink, follering it about until it came on dark, and then, o' course, he lost sight of it, and hoping against 'ope that it would come 'ome for its food, he went 'ome and waited for it. He sat up all night dozing in a chair in the front room with the door left open, but it was all no use; and arter thinking for a long time wot was best to do, he went out and told some o' the folks it was lost and offered a reward of five pounds for it.

You never saw such a hunt then in all your life. Nearly every man, woman, and child in Claybury left their work or school and went to try to earn that five pounds. By the arternoon George Barstow made it ten pounds provided the cat was brought 'ome safe and sound, and people as was too old to walk stood at their cottage doors to snap it up as it came by.

Joe Clark was hunting for it 'igh and low, and so was 'is wife and the boys. In fact, I b'lieve that everybody in Claybury excepting the parson and Bob Pretty was trying to get that ten pounds.

O' course, we could understand the parson – 'is pride wouldn't let 'im; but a low, poaching, thieving rascal like Bob Pretty turning up 'is nose at ten pounds was more than we could make out. Even on the second day, when George Barstow made it ten pounds down and a shilling a week for a year besides, he didn't offer to stir; all he did was to try and make fun o' them as was looking for it.

'Have you looked everywhere you can think of for it, Bill?' he sez to Bill Chambers.

'Yes, I 'ave,' sez Bill.

'Well, then, you want to look everywhere else,' sez Bob Pretty. 'I know where I should look if I wanted to find it.'

'Why don't you find it, then,' sez Bill.

''Cos I don't want to make mischief,' sez Bob Pretty. 'I

don't want to be unneighbourly to Joe Clark by interfering at all.'

'Not for all that money?' sez Bill.

'Not for fifty pounds,' sez Bob Pretty; 'you ought to know me better than that, Bill Chambers.'

'It's my belief that you know more about where that cat is than you ought to,' sez Joe Gubbins.

'You go on looking for it, Joe,' sez Bob Pretty, grinning; 'it's good exercise for you, and you've only lost two days' work.'

'I'll give you arf a crown if you let me search your 'ouse, Bob,' sez Bill Chambers, looking at 'im very 'ard.

'I couldn't do it at the price, Bill,' sez Bob Pretty, shaking his 'ead. 'I'm a pore man, but I'm very partikler who I 'ave come into my 'ouse.'

O' course, everybody left off looking at once when they heard about Bob – not that they believed that he'd be such a fool as to keep the cat in his 'ouse; and that evening, as soon as it was dark, Joe Clark went round to see 'im.

'Don't tell me as that cat's found, Joe,' sez Bob Pretty, as Joe opened the door.

'Not as I've 'eard of,' said Joe, stepping inside. 'I wanted to speak to you about it; the sooner it's found the better I shall be pleased.'

'It does you credit, Joe Clark,' sez Bob Pretty.

'It's my belief that it's dead,' sez Joe, looking at 'im very 'ard; 'but I want to make sure afore taking over the property.'

Bob Pretty looked at 'im and then he gave a little cough. 'Oh, you want it to be found dead,' he sez. 'Now, I wonder whether that cat's worth more dead or alive.'

Joe Clark coughed then. 'Dead, I should think,' he sez at last.

'George Barstow's just 'ad bills printed offering fifteen pounds for it,' sez Bob Pretty.

'I'll give that or more when I come into the property,' sez Joe Clark.

'There's nothing like ready-money, though, is there?' sez Bob.

'I'll promise it to you in writing, Bob,' sez Joe, trembling.

'There's some things that don't look well in writing, Joe,' says Bob Pretty, considering; 'besides, why should you promise it to *me*?'

'O' course, I meant if you found it,' sez Joe.

'Well, I'll do my best, Joe,' sez Bob Pretty; 'and none of us can do no more than that, can they?'

They sat talking and argufying over it for over an hour, and twice Bob Pretty got up and said 'e was going to see whether George Barstow wouldn't offer more. By the time they parted they was as thick as thieves, and next morning Bob Pretty was wearing Joe Clark's watch and chain, and Mrs Pretty was up at Joe's 'ouse to see whether there was any of 'is furniture as she 'ad a fancy for.

She didn't seem to be able to make up 'er mind at fust between a chest o' drawers that 'ad belonged to Joe's mother and a grandfather clock. She walked from one to the other for about ten minutes, and then Bob, who 'ad come in to 'elp her, told 'er to 'ave both.

'You're quite welcome,' he sez; 'ain't she, Joe?'

Joe Clark said 'Yes,' and arter he 'ad helped them carry 'em 'ome the Prettys went back and took the best bedstead to pieces, cos Bob said as it was easier to carry that way. Mrs Clark 'ad to go and sit down at the bottom o' the garden with the neck of 'er dress undone to give herself air, but when she saw the little Prettys each walking 'ome with one of 'er best chairs on their 'eads she got and walked up and down like a mad thing.

'I'm sure I don't know where we are to put it all,' sez Bob Pretty to Joe Gubbins, wot was looking on with other folks, 'but Joe Clark is that generous he won't 'ear of our leaving anything.'

'Has 'e gorn mad?' sez Bill Chambers, staring at 'im.

'Not as I knows on,' sez Bob Pretty. 'It's 'is good-artedness, that's all. He feels sure that that cat's dead, and that he'll 'ave George Barstow's cottage and furniture. I told 'im he'd better wait till he'd made sure, but 'e wouldn't.'

Before they'd finished the Prettys 'ad picked that 'ouse

as clean as a bone and Joe Clark 'ad to go and get clean straw for his wife and children to sleep on; not that Mrs Clark 'ad any sleep that night, nor Joe neither.

Henery Walker was the fust to see what it really meant, and he went rushing off as fast as 'e could run to tell George Barstow. George couldn't believe 'im at fust, but when 'e did he swore that if a 'air of that cat's head was harmed 'e'd have the law o' Bob Pretty, and arter Henery Walker 'ad gone 'e walked round to tell 'im so.

'You're not yourself, George Barstow, else you wouldn't try and take away my character like that,' sez Bob Pretty.

'Wot did Joe Clark give you all them things for?' sez George, pointing to the furniture.

'Took a fancy to me, I s'pose,' sez Bob. 'People do sometimes. There's something about me at times that makes 'em like me.'

'He gave 'em to you to kill my cat,' sez George Barstow. 'It's plain enough for anybody to see.'

Bob Pretty smiled. 'I expect it'll turn up safe and sound one o' these days,' he sez, 'and then you'll come round and beg my pardon. P'r'aps—'

'P'r'aps wot?' sez George Barstow, arter waiting a bit.

'P'r'aps somebody 'as got it and is keeping it till you've drawed the fifteen pounds out o' the bank,' sez Bob, looking at 'im very hard.

'I've taken it out o' the bank,' sez George, starting; 'if that cat's alive, Bob, and you've got it, there's fifteen pounds the moment you 'and it over.'

'Wot d'ye mean – me got it?' sez Bob Pretty. 'You be careful o' my character.'

'I mean if you know where it is,' sez George Barstow trembling all over.

'I don't say I couldn't find it, if that's wot you mean,' sez Bob. 'I can gin'rally find things when I want to.'

'You find me that cat, alive and well, and the money's yours, Bob,' sez George, 'ardly able to speak, now that 'e fancied the cat was still alive.

Bob Pretty shook his 'ead. 'No; that won't do,' he sez.

'S'pose I did 'ave the luck to find that pore animal, you'd say I'd had it all the time and refuse to pay.'

'I swear I wouldn't, Bob,' sez George Barstow, jumping up.

'Best thing you can do if you want me to try and find that cat,' says Bob Pretty, 'is to give me the fifteen pounds now, and I'll go and look for it at once. I can't trust you, George Barstow.'

'And I can't trust you,' sez George Barstow.

'Very good,' sez Bob, getting up; 'there's no 'arm done. P'r'aps Joe Clark'll find the cat is dead and p'r'aps you'll find it's alive. It's all one to me.'

George Barstow walked off 'ome, but he was in such a state o' mind 'e didn't know wot to do. Bob Pretty turning up 'is nose at fifteen pounds like that made 'im think that Joe Clark 'ad promised to pay 'im more if the cat was dead; and at last, arter worrying about it for a couple of hours, 'e came up to this 'ere Cauliflower and offered Bob the fifteen pounds.

'Wot's this for?' sez Bob.

'For finding my cat,' sez George.

'Look here,' sez Bob, handing it back. 'I've 'ad enough o' your insults; I don't know where your cat is.'

'I mean for trying to find it, Bob,' sez George Barstow.

'Oh, well, I don't mind that,' sez Bob, taking it. 'I'm a 'ard-working man, and I've got to be paid for my time; it's only fair to my wife and children. I'll start now.'

He finished up 'is beer, and while the other chaps was telling George Barstow wot a fool he was Joe Clark slipped out arter Bob Pretty and began to call 'im all the names he could think of.

'Don't you worry,' sez Bob; 'the cat ain't found yet.'

'Is it dead?' sez Joe Clark, 'ardly able to speak.

''Ow should I know?' sez Bob; 'that's wot I got to try and find out. That's wot you gave me your furniture for, and what George Barstow gave me the fifteen pounds for, ain't it? Now, don't you stop me now, 'cos I'm goin' to begin looking.'

He started looking there and then, and for the next two or three days George Barstow and Joe Clark see 'im walking up and down with his 'ands in 'is pockets looking over garden fences and calling 'Puss'. He asked everybody 'e see whether they 'ad seen a white cat with one blue eye and one yaller one, and every time 'e came into the Cauliflower he puts his 'ead over the bar and called 'Puss', 'cos, as 'e said, it was as likely to be there as anywhere else.

It was about a week after the cat 'ad disappeared that George Barstow was standing at 'is door talking to Joe Clark, who was saying the cat must be dead and 'e wanted 'is property, when he sees a man coming up the road carrying a basket stop and speak to Bill Chambers. Just as 'e got near them an awful 'miaow' come from the basket and George Barstow and Joe Clark started as if they'd been shot.

'He's found it?' shouts Bill Chambers, pointing to the man.

'It's been living with me over at Ling for a week pretty nearly,' sez the man. 'I tried to drive it away several times, not knowing that there was fifteen pounds offered for it.'

George Barstow tried to take 'old of the basket.

'I want that fifteen pounds fust,' sez the man.

'That's on'y right and fair, George,' sez Bob Pretty, who 'ad just come up. 'You've got all the luck, mate. We've been hunting 'igh and low for that cat for a week.'

Then George Barstow tried to explain to the man and call Bob Pretty names at the same time; but it was all no good. The man said it 'ad nothing to do with 'im wot he 'ad paid to Bob Pretty; and at last they fetched Policeman White over from Cudford, and George Barstow signed a paper to pay five shillings a week till the reward was paid.

George Barstow 'ad the cat for five years arter that, but he never let it get away again. They got to like each other in time and died within a fortnight of each other, so that Joe Clark got 'is property arter all.

The Cat and the Child

by CHRISTABEL ABERCONWAY

Dedicated to the late Dame Edith Sitwell

UNLIKE her mother the little girl had never liked dogs. Her mother's two spaniels were always jumping up and barking, running about the Sussex downs and clamouring for sticks to be thrown to them, splashing about in the sea, and generally, so Dorinthea thought, being a perfect nuisance. Worst of all, they sniffed under other dogs' tails and then seemed to be surprised when she wouldn't let them lick her face. But when she tried to explain this to her mother, and added that she preferred cats, and asked if she could please have one, a kitten of her own, her mother, usually so gentle and understanding, became annoyed and said that cats were 'treacherous' and that 'a dog is man's best friend'. After this, Nanny was told to stop Miss Dorinthea from stroking or talking to cats in the village street; and Nanny delighted in obeying this order. For she was not a kind woman.

But on this lovely summer morning Dorinthea was alone, lying relaxed and content on the short downland turf with the rolling hills stretching away towards the clear blue sky. Nanny had taken Dorinthea's younger brother down to the beach to smell the seaweed, or 'the ozone', as she called it, 'to make him grow stronger'. 'He's really nothing but a nuisance, and spoilt,' thought Dorinthea – 'worse than the dogs. Yet Nanny adores him, he is her favourite; just because he is delicate. It really isn't fair.' Talking to herself, she rolled over on her side, delighting in the fragrance of the soft, short turf as she moved. Something else also moved in the gorse bush close to her; a rabbit perhaps? Gently she moved towards the bush and even as she did so a small black and white paw came out to meet her. Surely, not a rabbit's paw? Her thin, sunburnt fingers parted the twigs, and there she saw a little cat – not much more than a kitten – stretched out in a hollow of earth beneath the stunted gorse bush.

'Cat, cat, my cat,' she called, and the fingers of her outstretched hands waved an eager invitation. The paw, so neat and gentle, moved further out of the hollow and tapped the child's fingers. Then it rested on her sleeve. Suddenly the child sat up and hugged her knees nervously; Nanny was climbing up the hill towards her.

'Time to be going home,' called Nanny; 'now then, look sharp. Time and tide don't wait for no one.'

Dorinthea kept her eyes on Nanny's face and did not dare to look down at the little paw or attempt to disengage it from her sleeve, for Nanny was now beside her, and was watching. As Dorinthea stood up she felt her sleeve tear, but she told herself she could pretend she had done this picking blackberries. A moment later, as they started walking down the hill, Dorinthea looked casually back; thank goodness, there was no sign of the cat. And yet, she asked herself, must she really leave it behind, and what would happen to it, out there on the hill all night?

Was it a stray? she wondered. There wasn't a house or cottage anywhere near, and surely cats didn't wander far from their homes? If it were a stray it might have chosen the gorse bush as its home, and so – perhaps – be there again tomorrow. But what would it eat? She decided that somehow she must try to return, and if possible take some food. Or shouldn't she give the food instead to the hunchbacked boy who always stood near the village pond, looking so desolate? A hunchbacked, pale-faced boy, and a stray kitten – which was the one she should look after, and help?

Luckily Dorinthea, who had an early luncheon that day because her mother was going into Lewes to buy some clothes, was able to hide away several pieces of chicken from her two helpings, and her mother, noting with delight her daughter's lively appetite, asked what she had been doing that morning to be so hungry.

'Lying at the top of a lovely hill. Oh, mummy, can I go there again tomorrow, while Nanny takes Baby down to the beach?'

Her mother, not always fully understanding the child, at once agreed, and Dorinthea went to bed that night fully content with the slices of chicken hidden away among her books. Nanny never looked at books.

Next morning, sure enough, the little cat was waiting in the hollow under the bush, and greeted Dorinthea with a plaintive *mew*, as if indignant with her for having stayed away for so long. The kitten was ravenously hungry, and directly Dorinthea produced the pieces of chicken it waved the tip of its tail with delight and began to eat and purr at the same time. Dorinthea lay stretched out in the sunshine on the top of the hill, watching her new companion hungrily eating up the small pieces of tender chicken, and then, to her delight, after it had washed its paws and looked around in case there was any more food, the little creature, still purring, crept up on to her lap and curled itself into a small ball of black-and-white fur. There, in the warm sunshine, with the meadow larks singing overhead, the girl and the kitten fell asleep. For both were perfectly content with one another.

Dorinthea had told Nanny to call to her, saying she would run down the hill to meet her, so that there was no fear of being unexpectedly discovered. But she awoke with a start at the sound of Nanny's voice, and as she stirred the kitten jumped down and shook itself, yawning. Perfect little white teeth, it had – and, as Dorinthea noticed for the first time, blue eyes. Anxiously, she parted the branches of the stunted gorse bush and placed the cat carefully in the hollow, stroking it, telling it to be quiet, and not to leave the nest. And she was certain that it understood.

Walking home, Dorinthea again saw the hunchbacked boy, sitting on the seat by the pond. He looked even paler than when she had seen him the day before. Was it right, she wondered, that she should take food to a cat when this boy looked so weak and ill?

On the third day Dorinthea was unable to go up to the hill again until after tea; then she dared stay only a short time, in case someone came to take her home. She stroked the kitten and gave it food, and then replaced it in the sheltering bush. Yet she had stayed longer than she had intended, for, as she started to run down the hill towards the village, there was Nanny coming to meet her, looking as cross as a witch.

'As if I hadn't enough to do without having to come all this way up here to fetch you!' Nanny grumbled. 'I can't think why your mother lets you come out here instead of staying with me and Baby.'

'I'm sorry, Nanny, I'm so sorry. I promise I won't be late again.'

'Promises, promises!' grumbled Nanny. Then, unexpectedly pointing over Dorinthea's shoulder, she exclaimed – 'Look, there's a *cat*! A horrible wild cat!'

Unfortunately, the stray had decided that *this* was the moment when she would follow Dorinthea.

'Now don't go touching it,' said Nanny, 'it's probably got the mange.' Dorinthea turned, and watched the little creature following them, bravely picking its way over the grass, anxious for the warmth of her companionship. If only Nanny were not there, she could pick it up in her arms and comfort it.

'Come along quick,' said Nanny. 'We don't want it following us.'

But of course that is exactly what the kitten did. Dorinthea stretched her hand out behind her back, tried to signal it to go back, but the cat followed faithfully, determined to stay with its new friend, while Nanny, growing red in the face, kept clapping her hands and shouting 'Go away, you little beast! If you come back to the house I'll drown you, or the dogs will kill you – oh, if there's one thing I *hate*, it's them cats.'

Dorinthea's mind worked quickly, while her face grew thin and white. Nanny was so tall and strong, how could she be so unkind about a poor defenceless animal? Would she really drown the cat? Could people be so unkind, so wicked?

'I'm sure I can drive it away, Nanny,' she said. 'Look, I'll throw pieces of earth at it, to frighten it off.' She stooped and gathered up some of the turf, digging her tiny hands deep into the down. Then she threw it, straight at the cat.

The kitten stopped, surprised by the earth which fell around it, shocked by the onslaught. And Dorinthea, stooping to find more earth, knew in her heart that all she really wanted was that the cat should be with her, in spite of Nanny.

'Go away home!' she shouted, although she knew that it had no home to go to. But at least it would be safe, in its hollow under the gorse bush, away from Nanny.

'Cat, cat, dear little cat,' she said to herself, 'don't you understand? Surely you understand?' Yet she dare not say it aloud, because Nanny was in front of her, marching down the hill.

The kitten turned, looked back at her for an instant, and then ran off towards the gorse bush. And Dorinthea, trembling, ran to join Nanny.

*

That evening Dorinthea had a headache and didn't want any supper, so she was put to bed early, and her mother took her up a glass of milk and some biscuits and placed them on the table by her bed. But Dorinthea could not sleep; she lay awake, thinking about the cat lying up on the hill, in the hollow under the gorse bush. Why couldn't she bring it home, why couldn't it come and lie curled up in her arms, in the warm bed? Suppose something happened to it, alone and unprotected, up there on the hill? What if she never saw it again, *her* kitten? Wouldn't it feel that she had deserted it?

Overwhelmed by her thoughts, she got out of bed and went to the open window. Nanny always insisted that there should be plenty of fresh air in the room. And there, sitting on the window seat, Dorinthea sat watching the great moon moving in and out of the clouds. Very low, they seemed, as if it were going to rain. Would there be enough shelter for the kitten, under the gorse bush? And presently, as she sat there, she seemed to hear a rustling in the great branch of magnolia which grew against the side of the house, under her window. Almost at once, she knew what it was. Leaning out, she caught up the kitten in her arms. Unbelievably, it had found her again, it had walked through the village and come to the house.

'My love, my own, my own sweet kitten,' she whispered. 'How sweet you are, how clever – to have found me. You know I never meant to drive you away, don't you?'

The cat purred in her arms, and began to climb across her shoulders. Then, with the tiny creature around her neck, she went back to bed. And there, all night, the cat slept cuddled up in the warmth of her arms, and all the world seemed perfect, at peace. So small it was, this tiny black and white creature, so beautiful.

But when the sun rose, Dorinthea was awake. She knew that the cat must leave. It could not stay with her, or Nanny would kill it. She looked at the little creature, nestling in her arms, and she made up her mind what to do. First, it must be fed. So she covered it over with her blankets, and crept downstairs to the kitchen, to raid the larder. There was no one up, she could hear Nanny snoring in her room along the corridor. And there, on the larder shelf, was a ham, stuck all over with cloves. It took her only a few minutes to find a carving knife, and cut off some of the meat. Then she found a bottle of milk, and a saucer, and with her breakfast for the cat she silently climbed the stairs again. Nanny was still snoring. If only she knew what was happening, how furious she would be.

The kitten ate ravenously, and then drank the milk from the saucer, while Dorinthea watched. How small that little tongue seemed, how daintily the cat picked at her food. But now it was time for the parting, the cat must go, or

Nanny would find it. So she carried it across to the open window, placed it on the branches of the magnolia tree, and waved the leaves, to make it descend.

Poor cat, it didn't want to leave her. But she insisted, and then – with a feeling of guilt in her heart – she shut the window. If only the cat would go back to the hollow under the gorse bush, and wait for her there. She hardly dared look, but she could tell by the movement of the magnolia leaves, that it was climbing down to the ground. What could she do, but hope that it would return to the hill, and the safety of the hollow?

*

Dorinthea was up and dressed before anyone else, anxious to have her breakfast. Her mother was surprised, there was an eagerness about the child, her eyes were bright and shining. It was wonderful, what a good night's sleep would do. Only Dorinthea knew why she had slept so soundly, why she felt so happy. Yet she wondered, – would her friend be safe up there on the hill? Suppose some dog in the village had seen it, the tiny, defenceless kitten? She would go up to the hill as soon as possible, to see that all was well. But unfortunately her mother, not realizing how important the day was to the little girl, decided to take her into Brighton, shopping. Dorinthea said she would rather stay at home, but her mother insisted.

'Just to Hannington's, my dear,' she said. 'It will do you good to get out, and we'll have lunch in the town.'

Once her mother had made up her mind, it was no good arguing, but Dorinthea hated every minute of the day. All she wanted was to run up to the hill and see if the kitten was all right. All along East Street there were dogs, but never a cat. When they sat down in the restaurant, she felt she couldn't eat, not while the cat was up there, on the hill, without any food.

'I think we'll have the chicken,' said her mother to the waitress, and Dorinthea knew exactly what to do. Her mother had only to turn her head for a second, and a nice juicy piece of cold chicken was there, wrapped up in the paper napkin, in her pocket.

'You *have* eaten that quickly,' said her mother, and for the first time that day, the little girl smiled.

*

She lay in bed that night, and counted up to a hundred, up to a thousand. Nanny couldn't understand why – for once – she was so anxious to go to bed. The napkin with the piece of chicken lay safely under the pillow. If only her kitten would come back, to claim it. The window was open, but it had started to rain. How could such a small creature make its way through the village, with the rain swilling around the road? Dorinthea trembled, wondering whether the kitten would ever find her again. If only she hadn't gone to Brighton, if only her mother hadn't insisted . . .

She could hear the rain pattering against the open window, dropping down from the magnolia. And then she heard another sound, the rustling of leaves, and she knew that what she had prayed for was coming true. Eagerly, she jumped out of bed . . . ran to the window . . . looked down at the leaves, and there was her cat, her precious cat, wet and bedraggled, but mewing and determined to reach her.

'Cat, oh you beautiful little thing,' she said, gathering it into her arms. 'How did you ever get here?' It was like a miracle, all her wishes had come true. All the uncertainty of the day was swept away, as she took the kitten into her arms and began to stroke it. Then she dried it with her towel – if only Nanny knew – and soon the kitten was in her bed, eating the piece of chicken. How hungry it was, almost starving. And presently, while the rain splashed down outside, they slept together, the little girl and her cat, warm and safe in an unkind world.

When morning came, the rain had stopped, but the cat's tiny paws had made muddy marks on the sheet. Anxiously, Dorinthea washed out the marks, but what would Nanny say if she noticed the wet patches? Could she pretend she was ill, and stay in bed until the sheet was dry? But first

the kitten must be persuaded to leave, and once again she took it to the window, and put it into the magnolia leaves.

'Come back,' she said. 'Come back tonight.' And she watched the cat climb down to the ground. Now, she thought, there would be no need to climb the hill to see her friend. The kitten knew where to find her, this was home.

*

That night Dorinthea again sat by the open window, waiting for the cat. Above her, she could see the silvery clouds passing across the moon, and in the distance the lights of the cars along the coast road looked like will-o'-the-wisps. The magnolia leaves rustled in the wind, and she wondered if her cat would come.

How long she sat there she never knew, perhaps an hour, perhaps more. She felt drowsy, half asleep. And then she was awakened by a scuffling noise, and a little scream, cut short.

Fearfully, Dorinthea leaned out of the window and looked down at the garden. At first she could see nothing, it was so dark, but now the moon was free of the clouds, and it seemed to her that she could see a dark form slinking away across the lawn. Smaller than one of the spaniels, it seemed, almost cat-like in its movements. For an instant she thought it was her kitten, but then she realized what it might be. Was it a fox? There were plenty of them up on Highdole Hill, and sometimes they came into the village, in search of chickens.

Dorinthea ran quickly down the stairs, avoiding the steps that creaked, and opening the garden door in the drawing room, let herself out. It was cold, and her thin dressing gown flapped in the wind. But she knew what she had to do, and she went straight to the magnolia, and began to search among the leaves.

At first she found nothing, the branches were wet and sticky. But now, moving her hands down to the stem, she suddenly touched something soft, and there in the moonlight she saw the cat stretched out on its side, motionless, as if it were asleep.

'Darling,' she whispered, 'what has happened?' Yet in her heart she already knew; the tiny form was no longer hers, her cat had gone, it would never return. She picked it up, feeling the warmth of its body in her hands, and carried it into the house and upstairs to her room. Even the creaking stairs were forgotten, she could think only of the precious bundle in her arms. Then she laid it on her bed and dared to look at it. There was blood on the white shirt, just under the neck. The cat was still warm, but soon, she knew, it would grow cold.

*

Dorinthea lay across the bed and wept. Perhaps she did not realize it, but her tears were not only for the lost creature which lay across the blanket, but also for all the other unhappy, neglected animals she had never known. How great the moon was, beyond her open window, but how small was this tiny, dead thing lying on her bed. Could there really be a God, who let animals be hurt? She wept until her small body was almost drained of tears, not for her own sake – she would be alive and well tomorrow – but because the cat, *her* cat, would never climb the magnolia again, would never stay with her. A tear, running down her face, dropped down on to the kitten's head. Blindly, she bent down and kissed the cat between the ears, where it had loved to be stroked. Then, knowing exactly what she must do, she carried the little bundle of black and white fur downstairs, and with her hands scooped out a shallow grave, under the magnolia. No one, not even Nanny, could disturb it now. Her cat was asleep, for ever.

*

Her nervous breakdown lasted longer than the specialist expected. Even though Nanny had gone home to Ireland, never to return, the child seemed not to wish to recover. There was no reason for the breakdown, the grown-ups could not understand it. But Dorinthea remained ill and apathetic, and sometimes, when her mother sat by the bedside, she wept uncontrollably. She was, said the specialist, suffering from hysteria, but what had caused it he could not tell.

How white and fragile she looked, thought her mother, how restless she was, moving her head from side to side, murmuring in her sleep. Night after night she kept watch over her daughter, and then, during the second week of Dorinthea's illness, something extraordinary happened. Her mother, half asleep in the big chair by the bedside, was awakened by what she thought was a faint rustle of leaves outside the window. It was as if something was climbing up the branches, struggling to reach the room. And now, to her surprise, she saw the child sit up in bed, smiling. At first she thought Dorinthea was sleep-walking, but she could not be sure. Amazed, she watched the child push back the bedclothes and start to walk across the room towards the open window. Her arms, as she moved, were outstretched, as if she were carrying something. When she reached the window she leaned out, and seemed to place something on the large branch of the magnolia. Then she turned back, and walked slowly across the room, and got into bed again.

Her mother was very worried. She knew that children sometimes walked in their sleep, but Dorinthea's eyes had been wide open, and now she was lying in bed, asleep, as if nothing had happened.

Suppose the child never recovered from this illness? She felt inclined to go downstairs and telephone to the specialist, but when she looked at her daughter again, and saw she was sleeping peacefully, she thought it better to leave her undisturbed. All she could do was to sit by the bedside and hope that Dorinthea would be better in the morning. So she sat there, half asleep, waiting for the first rays of light through the open window. And it must have been at about four o'clock in the morning that she opened her eyes, and realized that Dorinthea was moving restlessly in her bed. What is more, she was saying something.

'Cat,' said the little girl, 'dear, sweet cat.'

Her mother didn't understand, because there was no cat in the house, and as far as she knew, the child had never had anything to do with cats. Yet, it was true, and now she remembered it, that Dorinthea had once, when they were driving together into Brighton, mumbled on about the ginger cat down at the post office. At the time, it hadn't seemed important, there was such a lot of traffic on the road, but now, thinking it over, she wondered if her daughter had said something important. The trouble was, she couldn't remember exactly what Dorinthea had talked about. One could hardly take notice of everything children said; they so often didn't make sense.

Early that morning, when the local doctor called, she told him what had happened. Perhaps it was fortunate that it wasn't the specialist, only old Doctor Warren, because – did she but know it – the specialist would never have provided the solution. But Doctor Warren was a wise man, and he had a shrewd idea what was wrong, directly Dorinthea's mother mentioned the single word, 'Cat'.

'Well,' he said, 'if that's what the child needs, she had better have one.'

'A *cat*? you mean she wants a cat?'

'Possibly,' said the doctor. 'Children often need things that we grown ups would never dream about. Has she ever had a cat, of her own, I mean?'

'Why, no. She did once talk about it, but I didn't take any notice at the time. Besides, we have the dogs, and I've never really thought . . .'

'But the dogs are *yours*, aren't they? Not hers.'

'Well, yes, I suppose they are, really. But if we had a cat, the dogs might not like it, they might be jealous.'

The doctor smiled. 'Nonsense!' he replied, 'I visit dozens of houses where there are dogs and cats, and they get on much better together than some of my married patients. What the child needs is a kitten, something of her own. It's quite natural for a little girl to want a pet. You'll find that your spaniels will accept a small kitten quite willingly.

Don't spoil it in front of them, of course, but let it have the run of the house And if the child wishes to keep it with her at night, let her. You may find that is what she has wanted all the time, a cat.'

Dorinthea's mother realized, as she saw the doctor downstairs to his car, that she hadn't been quite as thoughtful about her daughter as she might have been. Leaving her to Nanny might have been a mistake, the child obviously needed more affection. She would drive into Brighton that morning, and buy a pedigree cat, perhaps a Persian, and bring it home.

Adults can often be mistaken, even where their own children are concerned. She meant well, of course, but it did not occur to her that Dorinthea did not need an expensive, pedigree Persian. Poor woman, she thought that her daughter's happiness could be bought with something costly. So it was fortunate, that morning, that as she drove the car through the village street, she stopped at the garage for petrol. Otherwise she might have driven straight into Brighton, and made a mistake. But now, as she waited while the garage boy filled up the tank, she looked across the road, and there, outside the inn, basking in the sunshine, lay a black and white cat. Just under the wooden seat it was, where the men sat out drinking their pints of beer.

She sat there at the steering wheel for a moment, and then she made up her mind. The cat looked small and young, and it might be exactly what Dorinthea wanted. Why go all the way into Brighton, searching for an expensive pet, when there must be plenty of ordinary cats around the village, whose owners would gladly part with them? She knew that unwanted cats were often drowned. Suppose this one, lying under the wooden seat, could be bought?

'I won't be a minute,' she said to the garage boy. Then she crossed the road, and went towards the inn. She had never been inside, it had the reputation of being a noisy place, especially on Saturday nights, but she was quite prepared to go round the back and see if the landlord wanted to sell her this cat, as long as she wasn't seen by her friends, entering the saloon door.

She looked under the seat, and the cat raised its head lazily. Then she saw that it was not alone. Lying close to the creature's stomach, feeding themselves with her milk, were three small, furry, black and white kittens.

*

Dorinthea was still asleep when her mother came home and sat down on the edge of the bed.

'Darling,' said her mother, 'look what I've brought you.'

The child stirred, and opened her eyes. She saw the room, and her mother's face close to hers, and then the most wonderful thing in her young life happened. It was there, in her arms, a beautiful black and white kitten. For a second she thought she must be dreaming, that it could not really be happening. But there it was, her own black and white cat, come home again. And as she gathered it into her arms, the child sensed, she was certain, that this kitten was somehow related to that other tiny creature, which lay under the magnolia tree.

'Oh, mummy!' said the child, 'may I really keep it? For ever?'

'For ever,' said her mother. And, as she watched her daughter stroking the kitten between its ears, she realized, for the first time in her life, what wonderful eyes a cat has.

Kitty, Kitty, Kitty

by JOHN PUDNEY

I CAN never hazard more than a shrewd guess what it was that made Mr Stephenson give way that morning. Usually when he left the Gothic porches of the terminus, he swallowed hard (for the train journey never wholly settled his large breakfast). Then with set face (for the burden within him was leaden) he marched towards his spirit's temple which was that part of the City of London within a quarter of a mile radius of the Bank of England.

On the morning he gave way, he found himself marching to the words 'Lucy Locket lost her pocket. Kitty Fisher found it'. Only a psychologist could tell us whether Mr Stephenson, so massively respectable, so painfully tortured by his inside, thought of Kitty first or of the rhyme first; and the psychologist's fee would really be wasted. For it was only necessary to explain that he had sung the rhyme when he was little and in pain from bolting his breakfast, and that he had been fond of a secretary called Kitty (her other name even now eluded him) when he was at the height of his success in the city. Now, as he marched sedately to his doom, the one and the other, the pleasant remote jingle of the rhyme and the pleasant – alas, all too remote – jangle of Kitty, merged, fused, and caused him, I suppose, to give way.

He stopped and stroked the rather shabby genteel cat which inhabited the bombed solicitor's office in Lunnion Row. Moreover, instead of keeping his mind upon that day's business, he said: 'Kitty, Kitty, Kitty . . .'

'Yes, Mr Stephenson,' answered the cat in an elegant, if slightly affected, voice, not at all at a loss at being so suddenly addressed by one who always passed by so preoccupied. 'Kitty, Kitty, Kitty . . .' said Mr Stephenson again, as if that was all he really intended to say and almost as if he had not heard the polite feline response.

'Oh, Mr Stephenson, but you'll be late, won't you?' said the cat with an elegant switch of the hind quarters, but always retaining a remarkable poise upon the wooden paling where once the solicitor's front door had been. 'Kitty, Kitty, Kitty . . .' murmured Mr Stephenson for the third time, abstractedly.

'I wouldn't touch those Tulip Hill shares today, Mr Stephenson. I'd go for the Lackspindle Deferred instead if I were you.'

Mr Stephenson stopped stroking the cat and glanced furtively up and down Lunnion Row where there were still acquaintances from his usual train making their way in twos and threes into the city.

'Why?' he said at last, a little irritated, but attentive. Though he prided himself a great deal upon backing his own judgement, that flair of his had been sadly lacking for some long time and the temples of his soul had been rather forlorn and draughty, subject to the chill winds of fear even upon the brightest of days.

'Oh, it's just gossip,' the cat said. 'One picks up a lot round the city at night. And, as you had stopped, Mr Stephenson,' the cat leered winsomely, 'I thought I'd just mention it.'

The autumn sun shone upon the fabric of St Paul's, upon the worthiness of the Mansion House and upon the solid substance of the temple of Mr Stephenson's spirit, within catcalls of the Bank of England. Mr Stephenson had an exceptionally good day. Very soon, indeed, he was to be seen five mornings a week pausing at the bombed solicitor's, glancing about him with the air of one who is on a good thing and hopes not to be disturbed while it lasts, stroking the cat and saying: 'Kitty, Kitty, Kitty'.

First-class passengers upon that line, however, in spite of their appearance of portentous reticence and high purpose, are strenuous gossips; and very soon Atkinson, Botherby,

Clegg, Dogstein, Effable, Ffoulkin and (there is no need to mention them all for they are household words in the city) Younghusband and Zink, had observed both that Stephenson stroked the shabby, genteel cat and that Stephenson could do no wrong. As the autumn passed, therefore, Mr Stephenson's good nature and *esprit de corps* were undermined bit by bit. Each day he was joined by more and more of his acquaintances and friends in Lunnion Row, all saying 'Kitty, Kitty, Kitty,' all stroking the gratified but sophisticated cat, and all, from Atkinson to Zink, forming themselves into a syndicate to operate exclusively upon the cat's advice.

Mr Stephenson, it must be said to his credit, possessed a sense of justice; and when Christmas approached, he felt the need to do something for the cat, who he supposed would have a lonely few days in Lunnion Row in the midst of a desolate unfestive city. It was a pity that Botherby was allowed to have anything to do with it, for it was he who broached the matter of mice; and instantly Zink, who practically owns one of the big departmental stores, offered to obtain them. In Christmas week, Mr Stephenson, with many of his syndicate, marched up Lunnion Row bearing their sordid sacrifice, two white mice in cellophane, which they had had the greatest trouble to conceal with any dignity while maintaining their portentous reticence in the train. 'Kitty, Kitty, Kitty,' he began. 'As Christmas approaches, we feel . . .' It was a well-worded, carefully composed speech: but while it gratified the members of the syndicate, it seemed to be accepted by the cat with a composure almost bordering upon disdain. The mice were deposited upon what had been the solicitor's doorstep, as Mr Stephenson rather lamely finished his oration. The cat arched herself and yawned. Some said that there was embarrassment in her expression; others declared it to be venom cunningly concealed. 'I can only respond to such sentiments, Mr Stephenson and gents, by mentioning that I have an absolutely red-hot tip before the markets are closed for Christmas . . .'

A stranger passing through Lunnion Row, on his way to business in the City of London, might, I suppose, almost have been tempted to bestow a second glance upon that scene, the cluster of worthy men against the wooden paling in front of the bombed offices, and the attention upon their astute faces as a refined voice pronounced the words: 'Mango Mines'. Nevertheless, a stranger would have been wise also to have ignored the significance of these words as market advice, and to have forgotten them: for, as all the world knows, the Mango Mines blew up upon that Christmas Eve, taking into the air not only many unfortunate Mangos but the whole resources of Mr Stephenson and all the spare cash of the syndicate, from Atkinson to Zink, associated with him.

The cat still sat upon the palings in the mornings, taking no trouble to conceal a look of baleful satisfaction as Mr Stephenson and the other gentlemen passed by. Rather ostentatiously, the cat displayed fat city mice for the gentlemen to see. Mr Stephenson never said: 'Kitty, Kitty, Kitty'. He had learnt many lessons in his life: but this last most painful one of all was never to insult the dignity, the altruism, and, above all, the vanity of a shabby genteel cat, more especially one of the more susceptible kind which responds to such a phrase as: 'Kitty, Kitty, Kitty'.

The Stalls of Barchester Cathedral

by M. R. JAMES

THIS matter began, as far as I am concerned, with the reading of a notice in the obituary section of the *Gentleman's Magazine* for an early year in the nineteenth century:

'On February 26th, at his residence in the Cathedral Close of Barchester, the Venerable John Benwell Haynes, DD, aged fifty-seven, Archdeacon of Sowerbridge and Rector of Pickhill and Candley. He was of — College, Cambridge, where, by talent and assiduity, he commanded the esteem of his seniors; when, at the usual time, he took his first degree, his name stood high in the list of *wranglers*. These academical honours procured for him within a short time a Fellowship of his College. In the year 1783 he received Holy Orders, and was shortly afterwards presented to the perpetual Curacy of Ranxton-sub-Ashe by his friend and patron the late truly venerable Bishop of Lichfield . . . His speedy preferments, first to a Prebend, and subsequently to the dignity of Precentor in the Cathedral of Barchester, form an eloquent testimony to the respect in which he was held and to his eminent qualifications. He succeeded to the Archdeaconry upon the sudden decease of Archdeacon Pulteney in 1810. His sermons, ever conformable to the principles of the religion and Church which he adorned, displayed in no ordinary degree, without the least trace of enthusiasm, the refinement of the scholar united with the graces of the Christian. Free from sectarian violence, and informed by the spirit of the truest charity, they will dwell long in the memories of his hearers. (Here a further omission.) The productions of his pen include an able defence of Episcopacy, which, though often perused by the author of this tribute to his memory, affords but one additional instance of the want of liberality and enterprise which is a too common characteristic of the publishers of our generation. His published works are, indeed, confined to a spirited and elegant version of the *Argonautica* of Valerius Flaccus, a volume of the *Discourses upon the Several Events in the Life of Joshua*, delivered in his Cathedral, and a number of the charges which he pronounced at various visitations to the clergy of his Archdeaconry. These are distinguished by etc., etc. The urbanity and hospitality of the subject of these lines will not readily be forgotten by those who enjoyed his acquaintance. His interest in the venerable and awful pile under whose hoary vault he was so punctual an attendant, and particularly in the musical portion of its rites, might be termed filial, and formed a strong and delightful contrast to the polite indifference displayed by too many of our Cathedral dignitaries at the present time.'

The final paragraph, after informing us that Dr Haynes died a bachelor, says:

'It might have been augured that an existence so placid and benevolent would have been terminated in a ripe old age by a dissolution equally gradual and calm. But how unsearchable are the workings of Providence! The peaceful and retired seclusion amid which the honoured evening of Dr Haynes' life was mellowing to its close was destined to be disturbed, nay, shattered, by a tragedy as appalling as it was unexpected. The morning of the 26th of February—'

But perhaps I shall do better to keep back the remainder of the narrative until I have told the circumstances which led up to it. These, as far as they are now accessible, I have derived from another source.

I had read the obituary notice which I have been quoting, quite by chance, along with a great many others of the same period. It had excited some little speculation in my mind, but, beyond thinking that, if I ever had an opportunity of examining the local records of the period indicated, I would try to remember Dr Haynes, I made no effort to pursue his case.

Quite lately I was cataloguing the manuscripts in the library of the college to which he belonged. I had reached the end of the numbered volumes on the shelves, and I proceeded to ask the librarian whether there were any more books which he thought I ought to include in my description. 'I don't think there are,' he said, 'but we had better come and look at the manuscript class and make sure. Have you time to do that now?' I had time. We went to the library, checked off the manuscripts, and, at the end of our survey, arrived at a shelf of which I had seen nothing. Its contents consisted for the most part of sermons, bundles of fragmentary papers, college exercises, *Cyrus*, an epic poem in several cantos, the product of a country clergyman's leisure, mathematical tracts by a deceased professor, and other similar material of a kind with which I am only too familiar. I took brief notes of these. Lastly, there was a tin box, which was pulled out and dusted. Its label, much faded, was thus inscribed: 'Papers of the Ven. Archdeacon Haynes. Bequeathed in 1834 by his sister, Miss Letitia Haynes.'

I knew at once that the name was one which I had somewhere encountered, and could very soon locate it. 'That must be the Archdeacon Haynes who came to a very odd end at Barchester. I've read his obituary in the *Gentleman's Magazine*. May I take the box home? Do you know if there is anything interesting in it?'

The librarian was very willing that I should take the box and examine it at leisure. 'I never looked inside it myself,' he said, 'but I've always been meaning to. I am pretty sure that is the box which our old Master once said ought never to have been accepted by the college. He said that to Martin years ago; and he said also that as long as he had control over the library it should never be opened. Martin told me about it, and said that he wanted terribly to know what was in it; but the Master was librarian, and always kept the box in the lodge, so there was no getting at it in his time, and when he died it was taken away by mistake by his heirs, and only returned a few years ago. I can't think why I haven't opened it; but, as I have to go away from Cambridge this afternoon, you had better have first go at it. I think I can trust you not to publish anything undesirable in our catalogue.'

I took the box home and examined its contents, and thereafter consulted the librarian as to what should be done about publication, and, since I have his leave to make a story out of it, provided I disguise the identity of the people concerned, I will try what can be done.

The materials are, of course, mainly journals and letters. How much I shall quote and how much epitomize must be determined by considerations of space. The proper understanding of the situation has necessitated a little – not very arduous – research, which has been greatly facilitated by the excellent illustrations and text of the Barchester volume in Bell's *Cathedral Series*.

When you enter the choir of Barchester Cathedral now, you pass through a screen of metal and coloured marbles, designed by Sir Gilbert Scott, and find yourself in what I must call a very bare and odiously furnished place. The stalls are modern, without canopies. The places of the dignitaries and the names of the prebends have fortunately been allowed to survive, and are inscribed on small brass plates affixed to the stalls. The organ is in the triforium, and what is seen of the case is Gothic. The reredos and its surroundings are like every other.

Careful engravings of a hundred years ago show a very different state of things. The organ is on a massive classical screen. The stalls are also classical and very massive. There is a *baldacchino* of wood over the altar, with urns upon its corners. Farther east is a solid altar screen, classical in design, of wood, with a pediment, in which is a triangle surrounded by rays, enclosing certain Hebrew letters in gold. Cherubs contemplate these. There is a pulpit with a great sounding-board at the eastern end of the stalls on the north side, and there is a black-and-white marble pavement. Two ladies and a gentleman are admiring the general effect. From other sources I gather that the archdeacon's stall then, as now, was next to the bishop's throne at the south-eastern end of the stalls. His house almost faces the western part of the church, and is a fine red-brick building of William the Third's time.

Here Dr Haynes, already a mature man, took up his abode with his sister in the year 1810. The dignity had long been the object of his wishes, but his predecessor refused to depart until he had attained the age of ninety-two. About a week after he had held a modest festival in celebration of that ninety-second birthday, there came a morning, late in the year, when Dr Haynes, hurrying cheerfully into his breakfast-room, rubbing his hands and humming a tune, was greeted, and checked in his genial flow of spirits, by the sight of his sister, seated, indeed, in her usual place behind the tea-urn, but bowed forward and sobbing unrestrainedly into her handkerchief. 'Oh, Johnny, you've not heard? The poor dear archdeacon!' 'The archdeacon, yes? What is it – ill, is he?' 'No, no; they found him on the staircase this morning; it is so shocking.' 'Is it possible! Dear, dear, poor Pulteney! Had there been any seizure?' 'They don't think so, and that is almost the worst thing about it. It seems to have been all the fault of that stupid maid of theirs, Jane.' Dr Haynes paused. 'I don't quite understand, Letitia. How was the maid at fault?' 'Why, as far as I can make out, there was a stair-rod missing, and she never mentioned it, and the poor archdeacon set his foot quite on the edge of the step – you know how slippery that oak is – and it seems he must have fallen almost the whole flight and broken his neck. It *is* so sad for poor Miss Pulteney. Of course, they will get rid of the girl at once. I never liked her.' Miss Haynes' grief resumed its sway, but eventually relaxed so far as to permit of her taking some breakfast. Not so her brother, who, after standing in silence before the window for some minutes, left the room, and did not appear again that morning.

I need only add that the careless maid-servant was dismissed forthwith, but that the missing stair-rod was very shortly afterwards found *under* the stair-carpet – an additional proof, if any were needed, of extreme stupidity and carelessness on her part.

For a good many years Dr Haynes had been marked out by his ability, which seems to have been really considerable, as the likely successor of Archdeacon Pulteney, and no disappointment was in store for him. He was duly installed, and entered with zeal upon the discharge of those functions which are appropriate to one in his position. A considerable space in his journals is occupied with exclamations upon the confusion in which Archdeacon Pulteney had left the business of his office and the documents appertaining to it. 'Dues upon Wringham and Barnswood have been uncollected for something like twelve years, and are largely irrecoverable; no visitation has been held for seven years; four chancels are almost past mending. The persons deputed by the archdeacon have been nearly as incapable as himself.' It was almost a matter for thankfulness that this state of things had not been permitted to continue, and a letter from a friend confirms this view. '*Ὁ Κατέχων*,' it says (in rather cruel allusion to the Second Epistle to the Thessalonians) 'is removed at last. My poor friend! I give you my word that, on the last occasion of my crossing his threshold, there was no single paper that he could lay hands upon, no syllable of mine that he could hear, and no fact in connexion with my business that he could remember. But now, thanks to a negligent maid and a loose stair-carpet, there is some prospect that necessary business will be transacted without a complete loss alike of voice and temper.' This letter was tucked into a pocket in the cover of one of the diaries.

There can be no doubt of the new archdeacon's zeal and enthusiasm. 'Give me but time to reduce to some semblance of order the innumerable errors and complications with which I am confronted, and I shall gladly and sincerely join with the aged Israelite in the canticle which too many, I fear, pronounce but with their lips.' This reflection I find, not in a diary, but a letter; the doctor's friends seem to have returned his correspondence to his surviving sister. He does not confine himself, however, to reflections. His investigation of the rights and duties of his office are very searching and businesslike, and there is a calculation in one place that a period of three years will just suffice to set the business of the Archdeaconry upon a proper footing. The estimate appears to have been an exact one. For just three years he is occupied in reforms; but I look in vain at the end of that time for the promised *Nunc dimittis*. He has now found a new sphere of activity. Hitherto his duties have precluded him from more than an occasional attendance at the Cathedral services. Now he begins to take an interest in the fabric and the music. Upon his struggles with the organist, an old gentleman who had been in office since 1786, I have no time to dwell; they were not attended with any marked success. More to the purpose is his sudden growth of enthusiasm for the Cathedral itself and its furniture. There is a draft of a letter to Sylvanus Urgan (which I do not think was ever sent) describing the stalls in the choir. As I have said, these were of fairly late date – of about the year 1700, in fact.

'The archdeacon's stall, situated at the south-east end, west of the episcopal throne (now so worthily occupied by the truly excellent prelate who adorns the See of Barchester), is distinguished by some curious ornamentation. In addition to the arms of Dean West, by whose efforts the whole of the internal furniture of the choir was completed, the prayer-desk is terminated at the eastern extremity by three small but remarkable statuettes in the grotesque manner. One is an exquisitely modelled figure of a cat, whose crouching posture suggests with admirable spirit the suppleness, vigilance, and craft of the redoubted adversary of the genus *Mus*. Opposite to this is a figure seated upon a throne and invested with the attributes of royalty; but it is no earthly

monarch whom the carver has sought to portray. His feet are studiously concealed by the long robe in which he is draped; but neither the crown nor the cap which he wears suffice to hide the prick-ears and curving horns which betray his Tartarean origin; and the hand which rests upon his knee is armed with talons of horrifying length and sharpness. Between these two figures stands a shape muffled in a long mantle. This might at first sight be mistaken for a monk or "friar of orders grey", for the head is cowled and a knotted cord depends from somewhere about the waist. A slight inspection, however, will lead to a very different conclusion. The knotted cord is quickly seen to be a halter, held by a hand all but concealed within the draperies; while the sunken features and, horrid to relate, the rent flesh upon the cheek-bones, proclaim the King of Terrors. These figures are evidently the production of no unskilled chisel; and should it chance that any of your correspondents are able to throw light upon their origin and significance, my obligations to your valuable miscellany will be largely increased.'

There is more description in the paper, and, seeing that the woodwork in question has now disappeared, it has a considerable interest. A paragraph at the end is worth quoting:

'Some late researches among the Chapter accounts have shown me that the carving of the stalls was not, as was very usually reported, the work of Dutch artists, but was executed by a native of this city or district named Austin. The timber was procured from an oak copse in the vicinity, the property of the Dean and Chapter, known as Holywood. Upon a recent visit to the parish within whose boundaries it is situated, I learned from the aged and truly respectable incumbent that traditions still lingered amongst the inhabitants of the great size and age of the oaks employed to furnish the materials of the stately structure which has been, however imperfectly, described in the above lines. Of one in particular, which stood near the centre of the grove, it is remembered that it was known as the Hanging Oak. The propriety of that title is confirmed by the fact that a quantity of human bones was found in the soil about its roots, and at certain times of the year it was the custom for those who wished to secure a successful issue to their affairs, whether of love or the ordinary business of life, to suspend from its boughs small images or puppets rudely fashioned of straw, twigs, or the like rustic materials.'

So much for the archdeacon's archaeological investigations. To return to his career as it is to be gathered from his diaries. Those of his first three years of hard and careful work show him throughout in high spirits, and, doubtless, during this time, that reputation for hospitality and urbanity which is mentioned in his obituary notice was well deserved. After that, as time goes on, I see a shadow coming over him – destined to develop into utter blackness – which I cannot but think must have been reflected in his outward demeanour. He commits a good deal of his fears and troubles to his diary; there was no other outlet for them. He was unmarried, and his sister was not always with him. But I am much mistaken if he has told all that he might have told. A series of extracts shall be given:

'Aug 30, 1816 – The days begin to draw in more perceptibly than ever. Now that the Archdeaconry papers are reduced to order, I must find some further employment for the evening hours of autumn and winter. It is a great blow that Letitia's health will not allow her to stay through these months. Why not go on with my *Defence of Episcopacy*? It may be useful.

'Sept 15 – Letitia has left me for Brighton.

'Oct 11 – Candles lit in the choir for the first time at evening prayers. It came as a shock: I find that I absolutely shrink from the dark season.

'Nov 17 – Much struck by the character of the carving on my desk; I do not know that I had ever carefully noticed it before. My attention was called to it by an accident. During the *Magnificat* I was, I regret to say, almost overcome with sleep. My hand was resting on the back of the carved figure of a cat which is the nearest to me of the three figures on the end of my stall. I was not aware of this, for I was not looking in that direction, until I was startled by what seemed a softness, a feeling as of rather rough and coarse fur, and a sudden movement, as if the creature was twisting round its head to bite me. I regained complete consciousness in an instant, and I have some idea that I must have uttered a suppressed exclamation, for I noticed that Mr Treasurer turned his head quickly in my direction. The impression of the unpleasant feeling was so strong that I found myself rubbing my hand upon my surplice. This accident led me to examine the figures after prayers more carefully than I had done before, and I realized for the first time with what skill they are executed.

'Dec 6 – I do indeed miss Letitia's company. The evenings, after I have worked as long as I can at my *Defence*, are very trying. The house is too large for a lonely man, and visitors of any kind are too rare. I get an uncomfortable impression when going to my room that there *is* company of some kind. The fact is (I may as well formulate it to myself) that I hear voices. This, I am well aware, is a common symptom of incipient decay of the brain – and I believe that I should be less disquieted than I am if I had any suspicion that this was the case. I have none – none whatever, nor is there anything in my family history to give colour to such an idea. Work, diligent work and a punctual attention to the duties which fall to me is my best remedy, and I have little doubt that it will prove efficacious.

'Jan 1 – My trouble is, I must confess it, increasing upon me. Last night, upon my return after midnight from the Deanery, I lit my candle to go upstairs. I was nearly at the top when something whispered to me, "Let me wish you a happy New Year." I could not be mistaken: it spoke distinctly and with a peculiar emphasis. Had I dropped my candle, as I all but did, I tremble to think what the consequences must have been. As it was, I managed to get up the last flight, and was quickly in my room with the door locked, and experienced no other disturbance.

'Jan 15 – I had occasion to come downstairs last night to my workroom for my watch, which I had inadvertently left on my table when I went up to bed. I think I was at the top of the last flight when I had a sudden impression of a sharp whisper in my ear, "Take care." I clutched the balusters and naturally looked round at once. Of course, there was nothing. After a moment I went on – it was no good turning back – but I had as nearly as possible fallen: a cat – a large one by the feel of it – slipped between my feet, but again, of course, I saw nothing. It *may* have been the kitchen cat, but I do not think it was.

'Feb 27 – A curious thing last night, which I should like to forget. Perhaps if I put it down here I may see it in its true proportion. I worked in the library from about 9 to 10. The hall and staircase seemed to be unusually full of what I can only call movement without sound: by this I mean that there seemed to be continuous going and coming, and that whenever I ceased writing to listen, or looked out into the hall, the stillness was absolutely unbroken. Nor, in going to my room at an earlier hour than usual – about half past ten – was I conscious of anything that I could call a noise. It so happened that I had told John to come to my room for the letter to the bishop which I wished to have delivered early in the morning at the Palace. He was to sit up, therefore, and come for it when he heard me retire. This I had for the moment forgotten, though I had remembered to carry the letter with me to my room. But when, as I was winding up my watch, I heard a light tap at the door, and a low voice saying, "May I come in?" (which I most undoubtedly did hear), I recollected the fact, and took up the letter from my dressing table, saying, "Certainly: come in." No one, however, answered my summons, and it was now that, as I strongly suspect, I committed an error; for I opened the door and held the letter out. There was certainly no one at that moment in the passage, but, in the instant of my standing there, the door at the end opened and John appeared carrying a candle. I asked him whether he had come to the door earlier; but am satisfied that he had not. I do not like the situation; but although my senses were very much on the alert, and though it was some time before I could sleep, I must allow that I perceived nothing further of an untoward character.'

With the return of spring, when his sister came to live with him for some months, Dr Haynes' entries became more cheerful, and, indeed, no symptom of depression is discernible until the early part of September, when he was again left alone. And now, indeed, there is evidence that he was incommoded again, and that more pressingly. To this matter I will return, in a moment, but I digress to put in a document which, rightly or wrongly, I believe to have a bearing on the thread of the story.

The account-books of Dr Haynes, preserved along with his other papers, show, from a date but little later than that of his institution as archdeacon, a quarterly payment of £25 to J.L. Nothing could have been made of this, had it stood by itself. But I connect with it a very dirty and ill-written letter, which, like another that I have quoted, was in a pocket in the cover of a diary. Of date or postmark there is no vestige, and the decipherment was not easy. It appears to run:

'Dr Sr

'I have bin expctin to her off you theis last wicks, and not Haveing done so must supose you have not got mine witch was saying how me and my man had met in with bad times this season all seems to go cross with us on the farm and which way to look for the rent we have no knowledge of it this been the sad case with us if you would have the great (liberality *probably, but the exact spelling defies reproduction*) to send fourty pounds otherwise steps will have to be took which I should not wish. Has you was the Means of me losing my place with Dr Pulteney I think it is only just what I am asking and you know best what I could say if I was Put to it but I do not wish anything of that unpleasant Nature being one that always wish to have everything Pleasant about me.

'Your obedt Servt,
Jane Lee.'

About the time at which I suppose this letter to have been written there is, in fact, a payment of £40 to J.L.

We return to the diary:

'Oct 22 – At evening prayers, during the Psalms, I had that same experience which I recollect from last year. I was resting my hand on one of the carved figures, as before (I usually avoid that of the cat now), and – I was going to have said – a change came over it, but that seems attributing too much importance to what must, after all, be due to some physical affection in myself: at any rate, the wood seemed to become chilly and soft as if made of wet linen. I can assign the moment at which I became sensible of this. The choir were singing the words (*Set thou an ungodly man to be ruler over him and*) *let Satan stand at his right hand.*

'The whispering in my house was more persistent tonight. I seemed not to be rid of it in my room. I have not noticed this before. A nervous man, which I am not, and hope I am not becoming, would have been much annoyed, if not alarmed, by it. The cat was on the stairs tonight. I think it sits there always. There *is* no kitchen cat.

'Nov 15 – Here again I must note a matter I do not understand. I am much troubled in sleep. No definite image presented itself, but I was pursued by the very vivid impression that wet lips were whispering into my ear with great rapidity and emphasis for some time together. After this, I suppose, I fell asleep, but was awakened with a start by a feeling as if a hand were laid on my shoulder. To my intense alarm I found myself standing at the top of the lowest flight of the first staircase. The moon was shining brightly enough through the large window to let me see that there was a large cat on the second or third step. I can make no comment. I crept up to bed again, I do not know how.

Yes, mine is a heavy burden.' (Then follows a line or two which has been scratched out. I fancy I read something like 'acted for the best'.)

Not long after this it is evident to me that the archdeacon's firmness began to give way under the pressure of these phenomena. I omit as unnecessarily painful and distressing the ejaculations and prayers which, in the months of December and January, appear for the first time and become increasingly frequent. Throughout this time, however, he is obstinate in clinging to his post. Why he did not plead ill-health and take refuge at Bath or Brighton I cannot tell; my impression is that it would have done him no good; that he was a man who, if he had confessed himself beaten by the annoyances, would have succumbed at once, and that he was conscious of this. He did seek to palliate them by inviting visitors to his house. The result he has noted in this fashion:

'Jan 7 – I have prevailed on my cousin Allen to give me a few days, and he is to occupy the chamber next to mine.

'Jan 8 – A still night. Allen slept well, but complained of the wind. My own experiences were as before: still whispering and whispering: what is it that he wants to say?

'Jan 9 – Allen thinks this is a very noisy house. He thinks, too, that my cat is an unusually large and fine specimen, but very wild.

'Jan 10 – Allen and I in the library until 11. He left me twice to see what the maids were doing in the hall: returning the second time he told me he had seen one of them passing through the door at the end of the passage, and said if his wife were here she would soon get them into better order. I asked him what coloured dress the maid wore; he said grey or white. I supposed it would be so.

'Jan 11 – Allen left me today. I must be firm.'

These words, *I must be firm*, occur again and again on subsequent days; sometimes they are the only entry. In these cases they are in an unusually large hand, and dug into the paper in a way which must have broken the pen that wrote them.

Apparently the archdeacon's friends did not remark any change in his behaviour, and this gives me a high idea of his courage and determination. The diary tells us nothing more than I have indicated of the last days of his life. The end of it all must be told in the polished language of the obituary notice:

> 'The morning of the 26th of February was cold and tempestuous. At an early hour the servants had occasion to go into the front hall of the residence occupied by the lamented subject of these lines. What was their horror upon observing the form of their beloved and respected master lying upon the landing of the principal staircase in an attitude which inspired the gravest fears. Assistance was procured, and an universal consternation was experienced upon the discovery that he had been the object of a brutal and a murderous attack. The vertebral column was fractured in more than one place. This might have been the result of a fall; it appeared that the stair-carpet was loosened at one point. But in addition to this, there were injuries inflicted upon the eyes, nose, and mouth, as if by the agency of some savage animal, which, dreadful to relate, rendered those features unrecognizable. The vital spark was, it is needless to add, completely extinct, and had been so, upon the testimony of respectable medical authorities, for several hours. The author or authors of this mysterious outrage are alike buried in mystery, and the most active conjecture has hitherto failed to suggest a solution of the melancholy problem afforded by this appalling occurrence.'

The writer goes on to reflect upon the probability that the writings of Mr Shelley, Lord Byron, and M. Voltaire may have been instrumental in bringing about the disaster, and concludes by hoping, somewhat vaguely, that this event may 'operate as an example to the rising generation': but this portion of his remarks need not be quoted in full.

I had already formed the conclusion that Dr Haynes was responsible for the death of Dr Pulteney. But the incident connected with the carved figure of death upon the archdeacon's stall was a very perplexing feature. The conjecture that it had been cut out of the wood of the Hanging Oak was not difficult, but seemed impossible to substantiate. However, I paid a visit to Barchester, partly with a view of finding out whether there were any relics of the woodwork to be heard of. I was introduced by one of the canons to the curator of the local museum, who was, my friend said, more likely to be able to give me information on the point than anyone else. I told this gentleman of the description of certain carved figures and arms formerly on the stalls, and asked whether any had survived. He was able to show me the arms of Dean West and some other fragments. These, he said, had been got from an old resident, who had also once owned a figure – perhaps one of those which I was inquiring for. There was a very odd thing about that figure, he said. 'The old man who had it told me that he picked it up in a wood-yard, whence he had obtained the still extant pieces, and had taken it home for his children. On the way home he was fiddling about with it and it came in two in his hands, and a bit of paper dropped out. This he picked up and, just noticing that there was writing on it, put it into his pocket, and subsequently into a vase on his mantelpiece. I was at his house not very long ago, and happened to pick up the vase and turn it over to see whether there were any marks on it, and the paper fell into my hand. The old man, on my handing it to him, told me the story I have told you, and said I might keep the paper. It was crumpled and rather torn, so I have mounted it on a card, which I have here. If you can tell me what it means I shall be very glad, and also, I may say, a good deal surprised.'

He gave me the card. The paper was quite legibly inscribed in an old hand, and this is what was on it:

> 'When I grew in the Wood
> I was water'd with Blood
> Now in the Church I stand
> Who that touches me with his Hand

If a Bloody hand he bear
I councell him to be ware
Lest he be fetcht away
Whether by night or day,
But chiefly when the wind blows high
In a night of February.

'This I drempt, 26 Febr. A° 1699.
'John Austin.'

'I suppose it is a charm or a spell: wouldn't you call it something of that kind?' said the curator.

'Yes,' I said, 'I suppose one might. What became of the figure in which it was concealed?'

'Oh, I forgot,' said he. 'The old man told me it was so ugly and frightened his children so much that he burnt it.'

Dick Baker's Cat

by MARK TWAIN

ONE of my comrades there – another of those victims of eighteen years of unrequited toil and blighted hopes – was one of the gentlest spirits that ever bore its patient cross in a weary exile; grave and simple Dick Baker, pocket-miner of Dead-Horse Gulch. He was forty-six, grey as a rat, earnest, thoughtful, slenderly educated, slouchily dressed and clay-soiled, but his heart was finer metal than any gold his shovel ever brought to light – than any, indeed, that ever was mined or minted.

Whenever he was out of luck and a little down-hearted, he would fall to mourning over the loss of a wonderful cat he used to own (for where women and children are not, men of kindly impulses take up with pets, for they must love something). And he always spoke of the strange sagacity of that cat with the air of a man who believed in his secret heart that there was something human about it – maybe even supernatural.

I heard him talking about this animal once. He said: 'Gentlemen, I used to have a cat here, by the name of Tom Quartz, which you'd 'a' took an interest in, I reckon – most anybody would. I had him here eight year – and he was the remarkablest cat *I* ever see. He was a large grey one of the Tom specie, an' he had more hard, natchral sense than any man in this camp – 'n' a *power* of dignity – he wouldn't let the Gov'ner of Californy be familiar with him. He never ketched a rat in his life – 'peared to be above it. He never cared for nothing but mining. He knowed more about mining, that cat did, than any man *I* ever, ever see. You couldn't tell *him* noth'n' 'bout placer-diggin's – 'n' as for pocket-mining, why he was just born for it. He would dig out after me an' Jim when we went over the hills prospect'n', and he would trot along behind us for as much as five mile, if we went so fur. An' he had the best judgement about mining-ground – why, you never see anything like it. When we went to work, he'd scatter a glance round, 'n' if he didn't think much of the indications, he would give a look as much as to say, "Well, I'll have to get you to excuse *me*" – 'n' without another word he'd hyste his nose in the air 'n' shove for home. But if the ground suited him, he would lay low 'n' keep dark till the first pan was washed, 'n' then he would sidle up 'n' take a look, an' if there was about six or seven grains of gold *he* was satisfied – he didn't want no better prospect 'n' that – 'n' then he would lay down on our coats and snore like a steamboat till we'd struck the pocket, an' then get up 'n' superintend. He was nearly lightnin' on superintending.

'Well, by an' by, up comes this yer quartz excitement. Everybody was into it – everybody was pick'n' 'n' blast'n' instead of shovellin' dirt on the hillside – everybody was putt'n' down a shaft instead of scrapin' the surface. Noth'n' would do Jim, but *we* must tackle the ledges, too, 'n' so we did. We commenced putt'n' down a shaft, 'n' Tom Quartz he begin to wonder what in the dickens it was all about. *He* hadn't ever seen any mining like that before, 'n' he was all upset, as you may say – he couldn't come to a right understanding of it no way – it was too many for *him*. He was down on it too, you bet you – he was down on it powerful – 'n' always appeared to consider it the cussedest foolishness out. But that cat, you know, was *always* agin' new-fangled arrangements – somehow he never could abide 'em. *You* know how it is with old habits. But by and by Tom Quartz begin to git sort of reconciled a little though he never *could* altogether understand that eternal sinkin' of a shaft an' never pannin' out anything. At last he got to comin' down in the shaft, hisself, to try to cipher it out. An' when he'd git the blues, 'n' feel kind o' scruffy, 'n' aggravated 'n' disgusted – knowin' as he did, that the bills was runnin' up all the time an' we warn't makin' a cent – he would curl up on a gunny-sack in the corner an' go to sleep. Well, one day when the shaft was down about eight foot, the rock got so hard that we had to put in a blast – the first blast'n' we'd ever done since Tom Quartz was born. An' then we lit the fuse 'n' clumb out 'n' got off 'bout fifty yards – 'n' forgot 'n' left Tom Quartz sound asleep on the gunny-sack. In 'bout a minute we seen a puff of smoke bust up out of the hole, 'n' then everything let go with an awful crash, 'n' about four million ton of rocks 'n' dirt 'n' smoke 'n' splinters shot up 'bout a mile an' a half into the air, an' by George, right in the dead centre of it was old Tom Quartz a-goin' end over end, an' a-snortin' an' a-sneezin', an' a-clawin' an' a-reach'n' for things like all possessed. But it warn't no use, you know, it warn't no use. An' that was the last we see of *him* for about two minutes 'n' a half, an' then all of a sudden it begin to rain rocks and rubbage an' directly he come down ker-whoop about ten foot off f'm where we stood. Well, I reckon he was p'raps the orneriest-lookin' beast you ever see. One ear was sot back on his neck, 'n' his tail was stove up, 'n' his eye-winkers was singed off, 'n' he was all blacked up with powder an' smoke, an' all sloppy with mud 'n' slush f'm one end to the other. Well, sir, it warn't no use to try to apologize – we couldn't say a word. He took a sort of disgusted look at himself, 'n' then he looked at us – an' it was just exactly the same as if he had said – "Gents, maybe *you* think it's smart to take advantage of a cat that ain't had no experience of quartz-minin', but *I* think different" – an' then he turned on his heel 'n' marched off home without ever saying another word.

'That was jest his style. An' maybe you won't believe it, but after that you never see a cat so prejudiced agin' quartz-mining as what he was. An' by an' by when he *did* get to goin' down in the shaft agin', you'd 'a' been astonished at his sagacity. The minute we'd tetch off a blast 'n' the fuse'd begin to sizzle, he'd give a look as much as to say, "Well, I'll have to git you to excuse *me*," an' it was surpris'n' the way he'd shin out of that hole 'n' go f'r a tree. Sagacity? It ain't no name for it. 'Twas inspiration!'

I said, 'Well, Mr Baker, his prejudice against quartz-mining *was* remarkable, considering how he came by it. Couldn't you ever cure him of it?'

'*Cure him!* No! When Tom Quartz was sot once, he was *always* sot – and you might 'a' blowed him up as much as three million times 'n' you'd never 'a' broken him of his cussed prejudice agin' quartz-mining.'

No 25 *To Be Let Or Sold*

by COMPTON MACKENZIE

BOB GURNEY'S tale of the empty house next door played upon the imagination of all the children in the neighbourhood throughout that autumn after Bob himself went back to school. I was in the country with my father, because Aunt Adelaide and Aunt Emily were travelling in Italy; but when I arrived to stay with them as usual at Christmas, the empty house had acquired the status of an enchanted castle. We would stand outside to gaze up at the begrimed windows and fancy we could see shadowy faces watching us from within. We would peer into the area over the railings, and try to shape that huddle of something in the farthest corner of the bare morning-room into the sleeping body which had muttered 'what's that?' to the venturesome Bob. Time after time somebody would vow he had distinctly seen it move, whereat we would scatter in terror. As for the young braggart who swore he had gone down the area steps, stared into the room and discovered that the body was nothing but a heap of old sacking, we scorned him. He did not live in our street, I am glad to remember. He did not even live in Burton Road or Carlington Road or Cronmore Road or any of our allied roads. He was, indeed, nothing but a refugee from Notting Hill, who was spending his Christmas holidays with a grandmother owing to the presence of mumps in his own home.

I fancy it must have been about now that the legend of the little old woman was born. She was said to accost children in the street and, after inquiring of them the road to somewhere or other, to stab them in the eye with a long hat-pin. That a little old woman with this unpleasant whim did exist in Kensington had long been known and had long been shivered over as a potential adventure. There were several children in the neighbourhood who declared they had seen her. She was reported to have a very red face and to wear a crape bonnet always askew. But until she took up her abode in the empty house her headquarters had been a mystery. We thought of informing one of the bobbies who passed at intervals with majestic tread along our street. We felt that the police ought to know about this little old woman. In the end, however, we were always deterred by a suspected lack of sympathy in the bobbies, large men with stolid faces, the incarnation of blind justice in their remoteness from the frailties of ordinary human nature. I once did get as far as saying to one of these ponderous embodiments of the law's slow but sure and ruthless course, 'Do you know . . .' but when he stopped and gazed down at my upturned face, my courage failed.

'Do you know the time, please?' I asked instead.

It was about this date that a popular song began:

If you want to know the time,
Ask a policeman.

So perhaps the Metropolitan Police were unduly sensitive about this question. Anyway, this particular bobby replied gruffly:

'Time you stopped playing about in the road and went off home to your ma.'

In the end we decided to consult the postman, who was the friend of every child on his round. He was a good-looking young man with such conspicuously curly hair that we always called him Curly, and so fond were we of him that we always came down extra early on the morning of Boxing Day so as to make certain of seeing Curly presented with his Christmas Box of half a crown.

I can see him now turning the corner by Doctor Arden's house about eleven o'clock, always in a hurry because he would always have been delayed with the second delivery by the conversations he would have had with children's nursemaids, and nurses on the way.

'Curly put down his bag this morning and caught a ball I threw to him.'

What a triumph for a child who could boast of such a special mark of Curly's favour.

His very rat-tats all along our street had a peculiarly inspiring sound. The postman who went round with the last post at night used to give rather an ominous rat-tat, and as there were always much fewer letters at night, those rat-tats lacked the cheerful continuity of Curly's morning delivery at door after door right along our street. At night there used to be irregular silences when a couple of houses were passed over before the next rat-tat. Curly had been married about a year, and when he and Mrs Curly had their firstborn son some of us were actually invited to go and have tea with the young couple and admire the baby. We thought it a tremendous adventure to visit a postman at home, and we were particularly impressed by the way Curly wore an ordinary coat with the red-striped trousers of his postman's uniform. We wondered if the policemen kept on their blue trousers with an ordinary jacket when they were at home; but somehow we could not conjure up the picture of a bobby in his domestic surroundings. Even without their helmets bobbies looked pretty rum. There had once been a bobby on our beat who had been exceptionally popular with the cooks along our street, and several of us had seen him at supper in our kitchens, his helmet resting on the kitchen-dresser. Not that I ever saw him in Hetty's kitchen. She used to say she had no patience with the way some girls carried on. So cheap, *she* called it.

We asked Curly about the little old woman with the hat-pin, and he declared that she had certainly made the empty house her home.

'How do you know, Curly? Have you seen her?'

'No, I wouldn't actually say I'd seen her.'

'Well, how do you know she's there?'

'Why, I left a letter for her only yesterday morning.'

'You didn't!'

'Oh, I didn't, didn't I? Well, if you all know more about

the inside of my post-bag than what I know myself, what's the good of asking me questions?'

'What was her name, Curly?'

'Her name? Let me see now. What *was* her name? Why, blowed if I haven't forgotten *what* it was.'

However, Curly's habits of playing jokes on us made us hope that he was not serious now. He had once told Clara Lockett that her brother had sent her a skeleton from the hospital where he was working and that this skeleton had come to life and gnawed its way out of the parcel and goodness knows where it had got to. Clara, however, was too stolid a girl to be frightened by such a tale.

'Skeletons can't walk, you stupid,' she told Curly in that heavy voice of hers.

'Skeletons can't walk?' Curly had echoed. 'All right, when you see it popping its head out of the cupboard and grinning at you, don't say I never warned you.'

And there had been the same twinkle in Curly's eyes when he had told Clara that story about the skeleton as now when he was assuring us that he had left a letter for the little old woman with the crape bonnet and the long hat-pin. All the same, we began to avoid passing the empty house after dark, and if we came back from a late message to one of the shops in the Terrace we used to keep on the other side of our street until we had passed Number 25. The silence and gloom of it in the twilight cast a chill.

And then one morning during these Christmas holidays Bob Gurney suddenly announced that he was prepared to take a personally conducted tour round the empty house.

'But what about Miss Bearsted? Won't she mind?' we asked, for now that entrance to the empty house was apparently to be made easy for us, we were not quite so sure if we wanted to go in, and we were inclined to use the bogy of Miss Bearsted as a counterpoise to any bogies in Number 25.

'She's got to go away today to see her mother who's ill in the country. She'll probably be away at least a week. Isn't it spiffing?' said Bob.

We pondered awhile the thought of Miss Bearsted's mother. She must be a pretty grim figure, we decided.

'Miss Bearsted's going away by the 3.20 train this afternoon from Euston. The cab's ordered at a quarter-past two,' Bob announced the next day.

Nobody who had seen Gladys, Muriel, and Dorothy clinging to Miss Bearsted and hanging upon her last farewell and even standing on the front-door steps to blow kisses after the lumbering cab, until it had turned the corner of our street by Doctor Arden's and taken the handkerchief fluttering from the window out of sight, could have supposed anything except the liveliest affection between pupils and governess. Was it hypocrisy? Or was it the propitiation that is used by savages towards the tribal god? Or was it really the affection of creatures for a being of superior strength?

There was a great gathering at Number 23 that afternoon when Miss Bearsted was gone. At first a certain amount of order was preserved, because someone put a damper on too much exuberance of spirit by suggesting that she might miss her train through a block in the traffic. Traffic in London was already a problem even forty years ago, and I dare say it will be just as much of a problem in 1971, forty years hence, by which time it is unlikely there will be anyone in our street, except perhaps the Bond baby, to know whether it is or not.

By five o'clock a large party of us sat down to tea and all danger of Miss Bearsted's return seemed to have vanished. We could now feel confident she was well on her way towards the Staffordshire vicarage where her sick mother was expecting her.

The sense of freedom was eloquently expressed by Bob Gurney, when Mabel, the parlourmaid of Number 23, brought in the usual plates piled up with thick slices of bread and butter, for he commanded her to take away that beastly bread and butter and bring in the jam.

'No such thing, Master Robert,' said Mabel, attempting to understudy the austere manner of the absent governess.

'You know perfectly well that you're only allowed jam on Sundays.'

'Pelt her! Pelt her!' shouted Bob. 'Pelt her with bread and butter.'

'Pelt her!' screamed Dorothy.

Muriel did not wait to urge action. She had flung three slices as hard as she could without a word.

'You wicked girl,' exclaimed the angry maid. 'You see if you don't get a good whipping for that when Miss Bearsted comes back.'

'Sneak! Sneak!' cried Dorothy, turning to the ammunition and carrying on the assault begun by Muriel.

'We'll give you a jolly good whacking yourself if you sneak,' Bob declared.

We guests, I am glad to remember, neither joined in such threats to the prim Mabel's dignity nor in the pelting of her with bread and butter.

'I'll go and fetch your mother down to you, Master Robert, if you don't desist from your boldness and wickedness.'

'Ha-ha! Sucks for you, she's out,' Bob shouted gleefully. 'So bring the jam.'

'The jam! The jam!' his sisters echoed in high-voiced excitement.

'Not a blessed spoonful of jam will you have, you daring children,' Mabel declared.

'Then we'll get it for ourselves,' Gladys announced, and with a rush the four young Gurneys swept past Mabel to pillage the store-cupboard. Groans of astonishment from their portly cook were heard. Cries of alarm from Edith the housemaid shrilled. Cupboard doors banged. A dish crashed.

We guests kept our places and looked at one another. Could this in very truth be the severe morning-room of Number 23 wherc we had so often sat demurely round the tea-table? It was an incredible transformation.

Presently our unruly hosts returned with their plunder. We saw no reason to refuse to share in it. Whatever happened we could not suffer at Miss Bearsted's hands as accessories. Our only expiation would be from within. So we tucked in with the plunderers, and cordially agreed with Dorothy that currants eaten *ad libitum* with madeira cake added much to its flavour. We assured Bob that anchovy paste when spread three times as thickly as usual was indubitably three times as good. We congratulated Muriel on the happy inspiration which had led her to combine sardines and bananas as her contribution to the feast. We had never found bananas so delicious as when eaten thus immediately on top of sardines. But it was Gladys who won the loudest applause for her contribution, for it was Gladys who produced the bottle of orange wine which we poured into our tea-cups and drank with a gusto that made us ask ourselves why fortune did not allow us orange wine instead of watery tea every afternoon. The only guest who did not enjoy the orange wine was Clara Lockett, and that because it was the medium at Number 3 to disguise the cod-liver oil she had been ordered by Doctor Arden. She sat looking at her cup with a sickly expression on her stolid countenance until we asked her if she did not like orange wine, and when she shuddered at the memories of cod-liver oil which surged over her we gallantly drank the contents of Clara's cup.

When this boisterous tea was finished it was voted by Bob Gurney too late to explore the empty house that afternoon, and looking at the drear January evening without we agreed with him. The broadest daylight was essential for such an adventure.

I believe most of us fancied we should hear no more of the Gurneys after that tea for some time. I think we expected to be told they had been locked up in their rooms on a diet of stale bread until Miss Bearsted returned from Staffordshire to complete the expiation. However, we were wrong; Bob Gurney was early abroad the very next morning and whistling for me to come down and join him for the exploration of Number 25.

'We're not going to have any girls with us,' he said severely. 'They'll only scream all the time.'

I agreed with Bob that an empty house was no place for girls, and when presently he suggested that there was no point in making a squash of the business by asking anybody else at all, I was too sensible of the compliment he paid me to show the least sign of disappointment that we were not going to invade the empty house with all the boys we could collect.

'You remember when they offered that reward for me last hols?' Bob asked as coolly as if he had been a mere puppy-dog, lost, stolen or strayed.

'Rather.'

'Well, a chap at my school said it would be rather a lark to denounce somebody, and I read a rather ripping book about Russian anarchists, so I know the right way to denounce anybody.'

'How do you, Bob?'

'Well, if you think a chap in a secret society is going to betray you, you write him a warning in blood. You write: "Beware. You have trifled with us too long. The vengeance of your comrades will overtake you in a way you know not of."'

'Wouldn't it take an awful lot of blood to write all that?' I demurred.

'Oh, well, I know where my master has some red ink. So we can use that instead.'

I thought this a good opportunity to try to find out what Mrs Gurney's reaction had been to that riotous tea-party of yesterday.

'Mabel didn't tell her. She's going to wait and sneak to Miss Bearsted when she comes back. At least she says so now; but I told her if she did I'd put hundreds of black-beetles in her room, and so perhaps she won't. Anyway, I shall start collecting them in case. But don't let's jaw about Mabel. I want to send this warning to Hungerford.'

'Why?'

'Well, because you always warn a traitor.'

'Is Hungerford a traitor?'

'He resigned from our secret society, didn't he?'

'Oh, rather.'

'Well, then, of course he's a traitor. I shall warn him to leave the country,' Bob went on.

'You can write him quite a long warning,' I suggested, 'now you're going to use red ink instead of blood. But he can't leave the country. He's got to go to school next term.'

'No, I don't suppose he will leave the country,' Bob agreed. 'But if he doesn't, he must pay the penalty for being a traitor.'

'What's that?'

'He'll be denounced.'

'Who to?'

'The police, of course, you fathead.'

'What for?'

'I tell you. For being a traitor. Is your head made of wood?'

'I meant what are you going to denounce him for doing?'

'For breaking those windows, of course.'

'But he didn't break them.'

'I know that. But I can't denounce him for blowing up the Tsar or anything, because the police would know it was all rot, and nothing would happen. But if I denounce him for something they know really did happen, they'll search his mother's house, and arrest Hungerford, and . . .'

'Yes,' I interrupted, 'but suppose he denounces you? He jolly well might, and if he did, the police might find out it was you, and Hungerford would get the ten shillings reward.'

'Oh well, denouncing is rather rot,' said Bob. 'Come and let's climb over the wall now and get into the empty house.'

Bob could drop a project of which he was tired as casually as a kitten can cease chasing a paper ball.

When he stood in the sunken yard outside the window of the kitchen and our footsteps were muffled by the sodden leaves of the Virginia creeper, I began to wish again for company and told Bob that I thought Almeric and Aylmer Spink (they were still living in our street at this date) would enjoy exploring the empty house with us. It was then that

Bob revealed to me for the first time his purpose in choosing only a single companion.

'You know, if burglars have been living here,' he murmured in a low voice, 'they may have left some jewels and gold in the house, and if they have we don't want to divide it with thousands of other people. It would be rather ripping to be rich. I'd buy a skit of things. And now wait a jiffy. If the window is fastened, that means there *are* people living in the house, because I left it open.'

I decided inwardly that if the hasp was fastened I would do all I could to dissuade Bob from venturing inside; but the window was open and presumably had been ever since Bob had opened it with his Norwegian knife last September.

We explored the basement thoroughly without finding any signs of human habitation, and what we fancied might be a body in the morning-room proved after all to be sacking, as the Notting Hill youth had said.

'Well, it wasn't sacking when I saw it under the window that night,' Bob declared.

The front hall, when we reached it through the door with panels of ground glass which led down into the basement, chilled our spirits. Perhaps it was the effect of the circulars which had been pushed through the flap of the letter-box and which finding no letter-box on the other side had fallen upon the floor to be blown hither and thither by the draught coming under the matless front door.

There is nothing so eloquent of abandonment as an unread circular about coals, and the whole of the hall of Number 25 was littered with the prices of Derby Brights and Wallsend and Silkstone.

We explored the drawing room and the dining room; but we found nothing of interest, though we enjoyed the view of our street from the dining room, because to look at it thus from an empty house gave us a feeling of ownership.

'If we find the burglars' treasure I vote we buy this house for ourselves,' said Bob.

I agreed that this suggestion was an attractive one.

'Only if we do,' he continued, 'I bags the drawing room,

because I want a place where I can have a really decent model railway.'

We went on upstairs to explore the first floor, and in that desolate square with peeling strips of wallpaper hanging down from the walls which in Number 9 was my Aunt Adelaide's sitting room, I began to play with the idea of expressing myself through the medium of a room. It should be draped with curtains of violet velvet with a golden ceiling, and I would have a lattice window inside the ordinary window, like Mr Mellor . . .

But Bob did not give me long to indulge in these dreams of decoration, for he was already leading the way up to the floor above. I was finding the silence and emptiness of the house more eerie the farther we went up, and the prospect of the top floor with the inevitable noises in the cistern cupboard was not tempting. I could not help wondering what we should do if we looked over the balusters and saw far down in the hall below a moving shadow on the tiles. By this time Bob was opening the door of the back room, and a second later he exclaimed:

'Somebody has been in here, by gum!'

My first instinct was to rush helter-skelter back down the stairs and out of the front door into the safety of our street; but my legs turned to cotton-wool and, feeling as if I were in the middle of a nightmare, I stumbled after Bob to see in one corner of the room a mattress with a couple of frowsy blankets tossed up in a heap on top of it. There were no chairs; but there were some battered pots and pans lying about by the fireplace, which was full of dead ashes; and in another corner there was a pile of rags with a pair of boots beside them, and hanging from a nail on the wall a crooked bowler hat with a collar balanced upon it.

'Look out,' I gasped, 'he may come back and catch us. Let's scoot.'

But Bob declined to scoot. He was now firmly convinced that a little search would reveal a robbers' hoard. In vain did I argue with him that nothing in the appearance of that decayed mattress or those dirty blankets indicated the existence of a successful burglar. He was bent on making us rich for life.

At last in desperation I suggested that here was a genuine opportunity to denounce somebody to the police, and to my relief Bob was taken with the notion.

'Well, come on then and let's get out of the house before he comes back,' I urged.

'But we must warn him,' said Bob. 'We must give him a chance of escape.'

'Why?'

'Because you always do warn anybody before you denounce them. Except the familiars of the Inquisition. They didn't.'

Until then I had always been prejudiced against the methods of the Grand Inquisitor, but now I began to see the point of them.

'I know, we'll denounce him here,' Bob exclaimed.

'But you've got no red ink,' I objected.

'No, but I've got some blue chalk. And Morgiana in the *Forty Thieves* used chalk. I wonder if she used blue chalk though?'

'Use any chalk you've got,' I urged him fretfully. 'Only do be quick.'

So Bob chalked on the wall above the mantelpiece of this squalid hermit's abode:

BEWARE!

Your hiding-place has been discovered by the sleuths of the police. Fly from the country unless you wish to rest for ever in a fellon's cell.

Signed

A WELL-WISHER

'But you're not a well-wisher,' I pointed out. 'If he doesn't fly, you're going to denounce him to the police.'

'No, *you're* going to denounce him,' Bob contradicted. 'And then I'm going to help him to escape.'

A long argument ensued about this. I pointed out to Bob that I never wanted to denounce anybody and that I didn't see why I should.

'Suppose he finds out that I denounced him?' I asked. 'He may come and murder me when he gets out of prison.'

'But you'll send the police what's called an anominous letter . . .'

'It isn't anominous. It's anonymous.'

'I bet you it isn't,' Bob challenged.

'What will you bet?' I asked.

'I'll bet you . . .'

But with what Bob was willing to back his spelling was never to be known, for at that instant we were interrupted by the sound of a cough somewhere down below in the empty house.

How I cursed myself for stopping to argue with Bob the ethics of denunciation and the orthography of anonymous! There seemed now not the slightest chance of avoiding being murdered. A contingency which had kept me in a stew on many a night when I had been lying awake in the long hours of darkness was about to happen in the full light of day. Escape was impossible. The hollow cough was already nearer, and we could hear by now the laboured breathing of somebody toiling up the stairs. I looked at Bob bitterly. This was where his recklessness had landed us: at the top of an empty house with a murderer coming upstairs, slowly indeed, but all too surely. And for us no more chance of escape than a couple of minnows in a jam-jar. Even Bob's debonair confidence was shaken. Even the serene roses of his complexion were mottled with apprehension at last.

'We'd better hide upstairs in the cistern-cupboard,' he whispered. 'And when he goes into his room, we'll try to creep past and get downstairs. Or perhaps, when he sees the warning,' he added hopefully, 'he'll be in such a funk that he'll run away himself.'

So treading the bare boards as tenderly as we could, we reached the topmost storey of the empty house, and crouched among the cobwebs at the back of the cistern.

To our horror the footsteps instead of turning aside into the room we had just left continued up the top staircase.

'He's heard us!' Bob gasped.

In my agitation I managed to get a strip of unusually substantial cobweb into my mouth, and owing to the way Bob was packing me still deeper into the corner I could not raise my arm to pull it out again. I knew it was only a matter of moments before I must cough and betray our presence. But just as I did cough, by great good fortune the mysterious unknown coughed himself so that my lapse was unnoticed. At least it would have been if Bob in turning round to urge silence with a warning grimace had not caught the cistern a bang with his elbow. The hollow receptacle rang like a gong.

To our amazement and relief, instead of hearing the savage growl which we associated with the elocution of murderers, we heard a voice quavering in obvious alarm:

'I didn't mean no harm by coming here. Don't go and treat a poor old man harsh. I'll go away quiet. So help me, Bob, I will.'

Naturally Bob himself did not suppose that the old man was appealing to him; but perhaps the use of his name as a variant for the Almighty's added a touch of dignity to his emergence from the cistern cupboard, which might otherwise have been endangered by the large smudge on his face. As for me, I was heartily thankful not to be murdered, and so much relieved by being able at last to extract that disgusting cobweb from my mouth, that I could almost have hugged the decrepit figure we found quavering on the landing.

He was indeed as old as he had announced he was. He had a long white beard much matted and ragged white hair. He was dressed in what may once have been the frock-coat of somebody as tall as General Brackenbury. On him it looked like a mouldering green dressing-gown. He was wearing on one foot a boot through the cap of which four toes were twitching nervously, on the other foot a carpet-slipper. Through holes in his trousers we could see a pair of emaciated knees, and round his middle, to serve as shirt and waistcoat combined, he had rolled a piece of green baize which was kept in place by string of various thickness. He had a collar, but nothing to which he could fasten it; so he had pinned it together with a decayed boat-race favour, a pale blue Cambridge swallow made of plush. Even in those days, when figures of utter destitution like this were more often to be seen than now, this old man presented an extreme example of human misery.

Bob and I recognized him at once as a poor old rag-picker, and, indeed, beside him on the landing, was a sack full of the fruits of his assiduous and melancholy contemplation of the gutters. We had seen him sometimes venturing timidly down into the areas of our street and taking a nervous, surreptitious peep into the dustbins when twilight was falling.

'I didn't mean no harm,' he quavered to us. 'I been out for two nights and I slep' yesterday in Waterloo Arches. I didn't think as it 'ud hurt anybody if I slep' here of a day sometimes. I can get a morsel of fire here with bits of coal sometimes.'

We assured him that we sympathized with his desire for shelter, and we earnestly promised that we would never reveal his refuge to the police.

'Good boys! Good boys!' the old man muttered. 'You wouldn't go for to do anything as 'd hurt a poor old man what never did no harm, on'y just picked a living as best he could.'

'And I say,' Bob put in, 'when you read what's chalked up over the mantelpiece in your room, you needn't be frightened. We only wrote it for a lark.'

'Thank'ee,' said the old man, 'thank 'ee, young genelman. But I can't read a word, printed or wrote, so that'll be quite all right, that'll be. But I can make my mark,' he added proudly. 'And I made 'un once years ago when there were a big set out about a right of way as the new squire had closed agin' the public. "Can you sweer, William Cobb, as you can mind your grandfeyther saying as how he'd used this here path by Tangley Copse, man and boy, without obstruction by anybody?" "I can sweer it," I up and told them, "if I was to lie down and die this blessed minute." And wi' that they wrote William Cobb his mark, and I put a cross, and Lawyer said he couldn't have put a better cross himself, and nex' day he give me a new half-crown. But I were wild in those days, and I hadn't a fourpenny piece left nex' morning.'

While the old man was telling this story of a remote triumph, there had crept back into his speech the burr of some distant countryside, and we might have been listening to an aged labourer in a smock-frock and tall beaver hat maundering on across a stile. In those days there were still plenty of old men like that in Gloucestershire where my father lived among his orchards.

But the present intervened, and it was in husky Cockney again that William Cobb suddenly and suspiciously asked:

'You didn't go and hurt my cat, did you?'

'Your cat?' we echoed. 'We never saw a cat.'

The old man chuckled faintly his relief.

'No, he'd lie low, would Mouser. That blooming cat's made of brains. Artful? Well, I reckon he's the artfullest cat in London. But he don't like strangers. Can't take to them at all, and for which, Mouser ain't to blame. He'd been treated bad Mouser had when I found him lying in a dustbin one pouring wet winter's night. Yes, he'd been treated bad. And if I hadn't have lifted the lid off that dustbin, I reckon as he'd have been dead by morning, Mouser would. But I took him back home along of me, and him being a black cat, he must have brought me luck, for I found a sov'ring lying on the edge of a drain just where the white buses stop at the corner of Redcliffe Gardings. So I was able to buy a bit of meat and make some soup for Mouser. Drunk it like a infant in arms, he did.'

'Do you often find sovereigns?' Bob asked.

'On'y found that one all the time I been picking. Coins is scarce. I found a two-shilling bit. Standing up on edge that was, right against the kerb. And I found a bob once among the green-stuff in Berwick Market after the barrers had gone off. Two tanners both on the pavement, and a thrupenny bit in the gutter just outside of a church. And nine coppers – two pennies, four browns, and three joes. That's all the coin I ever found. I found a wedding-ring once, but it was only nine carat. And I found a tooth with some gold in it, but I couldn't get nothing on it. So I kep' it for luck; but it didn't bring me no luck, because a cab-wheel run over one of my feet, and which is why I can't wear a boot on it.'

We looked at the four toes of the uninjured foot protruding through the boot by which it really seemed less hampered than the injured foot by the carpet-slipper.

'But I've had blooming little luck since I dossed in this house,' the old man went on. 'Here, come on in and I'll show you.'

He opened the door of the attic at the back, and as he led the way in, a big black cat ran forward to greet him, then caught sight of Bob and myself and retreated into a corner, growling.

'All right, Mouser, them's is friends of mine. They won't hurt you, my old boon companion.'

However, the boon companion, who had lost the whole of one ear and half the other, and who had a scar which apparently doubled the size of his nose so that he resembled a battered hobgoblin, continued to growl in the corner, occasionally arching his back and spitting at us.

'He'll quieten down presently,' the old man assured us. 'But he never did like strangers and he never will. Yet you can't blame the cat, for he was treated bad by somebody. Very bad.'

We bothered no more about Mouser's hostility in looking at the queer sight the attic presented, one side of it a foot deep in rags, pieces of coloured paper, bits of iron, bottles, and bones, the other side bestrewn with what the old man evidently considered objects of comparative rarity. Among these were rusty curtain-rings, broken keys, the seamed yellow handles of table-knives, cracked saucers and cups, cigarette tins, bits of rubber tyres from bicycles and perambulators, a couple of balls of silver paper, several balls of

various coloured tape and string, the rims and crowns of straw-hats, and most conspicuous of all in the very centre of this museum of rubbish the nosebag of a horse.

So Bob had been right in suspecting the existence of a hoard, albeit we should have been nothing the richer by our discovery of it.

'Yes, that's my little bit since I dossed in this here house,' William Cobb informed us. 'And it's not what it would have been a few years ago. Picking gets worse every year. I don't know whether it's my eyes ain't what they used to be or whether as these here municipal cleaners spoils the ground or whether people's getting more careful what they throw away; but picking ain't what it was. It's the same with eatables. You'll find a crust now where once you could find half a blooming loaf. Then there's cigars. You'd be surprised how far I've got to tramp now before I'll find enough cigar-ends to fetch a tanner. Well, I suppose I haven't got much longer. I reckon I'm over eighty years now, and I won't be sorry to doss down for good and all under the ground. Except for Mouser. Mouser 'ud miss me. Well, you can talk about human beings; but that blooming cat's got twice the sense of a human being. Come on, Mouser, these young genelmen won't hurt you.'

And sure enough the black cat seemed to understand what the old man was saying to him, for he came out from his corner and allowed us to stroke him.

'There you are, you see. He knows what a young genelman is. That cat? Why, he's a walking book. He caught a mouse the other night and kep' it till I come back in the morning and then went and lay it on my chest when I was dossed down. Wanted to share it with me. So to please him I got up and cooked this here blooming mouse the same as I might a bit of sausage or any other bit of relish I might find, and Mouser he sat and watched me cook this mouse with a grin on his dile like a happy kid. And arter I'd pretended to have a bite he eat that mouse of his like it was roast beef. Yes, that's the on'y thing as'll worry me when I doss down for the last time – what's to become of Mouser?'

Bob asked the old man if he had been sleeping in the empty house last September; but it transpired he had only taken up his quarters here since the beginning of October after an empty house where he had been living in Hammersmith had found a tenant.

'I reckon what you saw was a tramp,' he told Bob. 'They'll often leave a door open and set a chalk mark on it to let another know where there's good dossing. But I don't want no blooming tramps in here. So I always bolts the door when I comes back early in the morning from my rounds.'

'But what do you do when you go out at night? Have you got a key?'

The old man looked at us intently for a moment. Then, as if he had reassured himself of our goodwill, he said mysteriously:

'I got a skelington key. Open any ornary door. A feller left it behind him in a dosshouse at Whitechapel. But I never use it except on an empty house like what this is. I've lived rough, I have, very rough; but I was always brought up honest, and I've been honest ever since. It gets a regular habit after a bit. I never done a day in quod all my life. But come to think of it now, how did *you* get in?' the old man suddenly asked.

We told him about the kitchen window and the way over the garden wall.

'Then you both live in this here street. Fancy that now! Mouser, do you hear that? Neighbours, that's what these young genelmen are.'

Mouser twitched his tail in acknowledgement.

'There you are, you see. He's got you all according now.'

'I live in the house next door,' Bob announced, a note of pride in his voice. He evidently felt that propinquity to the habitation of this aged ragpicker added something to the distinction of living at Number 23.

'Fancy that now,' exclaimed Mr William Cobb, wagging his unkempt white beard at us. 'Well, we *is* neighbours and no mistake.'

'If I tapped on the wall of my room, you'd hear me tapping in your room downstairs where you sleep,' Bob told him.

'I reckon I would,' the old man agreed.

'I *will* tap sometimes if you like,' Bob offered.

'Well, it 'ud be a bit of company in a manner of speaking,' the old man allowed.

'Well, I will,' Bob promised. 'And I say, do you mind if we bring some other chaps to see you?'

'Not coppers?'

'No, no, of course not. Well, as a matter of fact,' Bob continued as nonchalantly as his blushing honours would allow, 'there's a reward offered for me. So I couldn't very well bring any bobbies here. No, these chaps are friends of ours.'

'Friends of yours is friends of mine,' the old ragpicker declared. 'That's right, ain't it, Mouser?'

Once again the battered black cat twitched his tail in assent.

So long as Miss Bearsted was in attendance on her sick mother old William Cobb led what was probably a more social existence than at any period of his life, for Bob Gurney introduced through the kitchen window of the empty house every boy and girl of his acquaintance. It goes without saying that all had to join a secret society first and swear the most bloodcurdling oaths never to divulge to anybody outside the secret society the presence of the ragpicker at Number 25. The old man became as much of a children's pet as Jumbo the Zoo elephant. Instead of raiding store-cupboards on our own account we now raided them in his interest. Even when Miss Bearsted did come back and the kitchen-window entrance was no longer feasible, by posting sentinels we managed to visit him from the front of the house. In return for our presents of food, the old man entertained us with stories of his past which we found of absorbing interest. He also taught us many of the signs which tramps chalk up outside houses to give useful information to their fellows of the craft, and we had a splendid time chalking up hospitable hieroglyphics on the houses of people we did not like. There must have been far more tramps in those days about London, for I well remember what a pest they became to some of our neighbours on whose gate-posts we had chalked up cordial recommendations of the good cheer to be expected by begging at their area doors.

Bob went back to school at the end of January, and I went back to the country soon afterwards; but friends of ours maintained William Cobb with supplies, and when

Bob and I saw him again at Easter we thought the old rag-picker was looking less emaciated. As for Mouser, he was positively sleek. Yet the black cat, though he would let any of us stroke him now without growling or spitting, would never accept food from our hands. We had to give it all to the old man before he would touch a morsel.

Bob went back to school again after the holidays; but this time I stayed on with my aunts.

One morning at the end of May, when Olive and I went to pay the old man a visit, we found him lying on his decayed mattress, a strange look in his eyes.

'I was out again picking last night,' he told us. I have forgotten to mention that, since Bob had arranged for him to be supported by the secret society expressly incorporated for such a purpose, the old man had seldom gone out. 'Out again picking I was,' he repeated in a kind of puzzled voice. 'And when I came back this morning I felt all of a shiver, and which is why I'm dossed down like this here. But it was a lovely fine night, and when I looked out of the window it come over me all of a sudden as I'd like to make the round again. It come over me sudden and peculiar like as perhaps if I went out picking I might find a sparkler. Ever since I took to picking I've thought I might find a sparkler; but I never did. And I didn't find one last night. Well, no one can have everything in this world, they say. And if I hadn't have found that sov'ring I told you about, I might have found a sparkler. It don't do to be *too* greedy. Yes, I went out picking again last night.'

He lay back, staring up at the ceiling for a while in silence.

'Did you find anything?' Olive asked presently.

The old man pointed a withered finger at a disreputable dog-collar on the floor beside his bed.

'On'y that, and the usual bits and pieces. And it come over me lying here just now as that dog-collar wasn't much to leave behind for Mouser.'

'Leave behind you?' we echoed.

'I wouldn't say nothing as 'ud frighten any of you kiddies.

Not for nothing, I wouldn't,' the old man declared apologetically. 'But it come over me sudden when I come through the door this morning as I wouldn't go out again except feet first. And I stood listening for a minute to some sparrows as was cheep-cheeping round the chimbley-pots, and then it come over me as they sounded like what they used to sound when I was half as big as what you are now. Yet, coming back from my picking of a morning early, I've heard thousands of sparrows, as you might say; but I never thought nothing of the way they used to sound years afore even I come up to London. Not till this morning I didn't. And when I come on up here and laid down it come over me as I wasn't feeling so strong as I used to feel, and I've been laying here thinking what poor old Mouser's going to do?'

We looked across at the battered black cat who was lying curled up asleep where the May sunlight was shining on the floor. He did not seem anxious about his future.

'You wouldn't let them treat Mouser bad, missy?' the old man asked anxiously of Olive.

'Of course I wouldn't,' she declared.

'He'd been treated bad when I found him. Very bad. And if ever an animile was grateful, that cat of mine was grateful. Well, you see for yourselves what he thinks of me. You might have thought with all you young ladies and genelmen coming here and bringing him tit-bits and making a lot of him, he'd have thought me a bit beneath him. But you see for yourselves he never turned against me, not a hair. Thanks to all you kind young ladies and genelmen, he's a cat now as could go anywhere, barring of course him having only half one ear and the other one gone for good. But he's going to miss me. I know that. So if you found him alone one morning, I don't think he'd disgrace a genelman's house, barring of course his poor old ears.'

Neither Olive nor I grasped what the old ragpicker was trying to warn us of. We thought he meant to go away literally and leave his cat behind.

'But why do you want to go away and leave Mouser?' we asked.

The old man stared at us.

'It ain't as I particularly wants to go,' he muttered.

'Then don't go,' we urged.

'You won't let anybody treat Mouser bad?' he asked again anxiously.

'No, no. We won't really,' we promised.

'The sun falls nice and warm where he's laying now,' the old man observed with an approving nod.

Soon after this we left him.

It was two days before Olive and I went again to see William Cobb. And when we opened the door of his room we saw that Mouser was lying on his chest. We thought the old man was asleep, and then suddenly the black cat uttered a kind of wail, a most eerie sound, and standing up began to claw at the green baize which the old man wore for shirt and waistcoat. We could not make out why Mouser's behaviour did not waken him. Olive suddenly turned white.

'I believe he's dead,' she whispered.

My heart gave a great jump, and I am sure I turned as white as Olive.

'What shall we do?' I asked, horrified.

'We must get Mouser to come with us,' she said. 'And then I suppose we'd better tell a policeman.'

I was about eleven at this date, and Olive was about a year older. It was a tremendous experience for two children, and looking back at it now I feel rather proud of our behaviour in not rushing out of that empty house at once. We could not bring ourselves, however, to go very close to the body of the old ragpicker, and Mouser refused to leave it. He had given up clawing at the baize, and he now sat with his back to us, gazing, I suppose, with those big yellow eyes at his old friend's lifeless face. We were afraid after we had told a policeman what had happened we should not be allowed inside the house again, and knowing Mouser's feelings about strangers we dreaded what they might do to him if he would not leave the body.

'Mouser,' said Olive at last, in a solemn tone of voice. 'Mouser, do listen. Your master is dead. You can't wake him up with your claws. He asked us to look after you. Please, Mouser, do come with us.'

I suppose that those who claim for the dog a greater power of personal devotion than the cat will say that Mouser left the body of his dead master to follow Olive because he was thinking about his own comfort. But I am sure the old ragpicker would have said it was a sign of his wonderful intelligence, and I agree with William Cobb.

Anyway, Mouser went to live with Olive at Number 7, where he lived happily until his death ten years later. Lady Marjorie was anxious at first for the safety of her bullfinch; but Mouser's sagacity was too great for him to repay kindness by trying to kill something his protectors loved. I never heard that he was even caught looking at the bullfinch. Gradually, too, he grew less hostile to strangers, and really except for that disreputable lack of ears, and hobgoblin's nose, he might have been a drawing room cat all his life.

After the death of the old ragpicker in the empty house, the owners took care to keep it more carefully closed. It remained empty for another three years, and it must have been empty for quite ten years when one day we saw a cheerful party of workmen arrive and take down the board on which was painted TO BE LET OR SOLD.

The Cheshire Cat

by Lewis Carroll

So she set the little creature down, and felt quite relieved to see it trot away quietly into the wood. 'If it had grown up,' she said to herself, 'it would have made a dreadfully ugly child: but it makes rather a handsome pig, I think.' And she began thinking over other children she knew, who might do very well as pigs, and was just saying to herself, 'if one only knew the right way to change them—' when she was a little startled by seeing the Cheshire Cat sitting on a bough of a tree a few yards off.

The Cat only grinned when it saw Alice. It looked good-natured, she thought: still it had *very* long claws and a great many teeth, so she felt that it ought to be treated with respect.

'Cheshire Puss,' she began, rather timidly, as she did not at all know whether it would like the name; however, it only grinned a little wider. 'Come, it's pleased so far,' thought Alice, and she went on. 'Would you tell me, please, which way I ought to go from here?'

'That depends a good deal on where you want to get to,' said the Cat.

'I don't much care where—' said Alice.

'Then it doesn't matter which way you go,' said the Cat.

'—so long as I get *somewhere*,' Alice added as an explanation.

'Oh, you're sure to do that,' said the Cat, 'if you only walk long enough.'

Alice felt that this could not be denied, so she tried another question. 'What sort of people live about here?'

'In *that* direction,' the Cat said, waving its right paw round, 'lives a Hatter: and in *that* direction,' waving the other paw, 'lives a March Hare. Visit either you like: they're both mad.'

'But I don't want to go among mad people,' Alice remarked.

'Oh, you can't help that,' said the Cat: 'we're all mad here. I'm mad. You're mad.'

'How do you know I'm mad?' said Alice.

'You must be,' said the Cat, 'or you wouldn't have come here.'

Alice didn't think that it proved it at all: however, she went on: 'And how do you know that you're mad?'

'To begin with,' said the Cat, 'a dog's not mad. You grant that?'

'I suppose so,' said Alice.

'Well, then,' the Cat went on, 'you see a dog growls when it's angry, and wags its tail when it's pleased. Now *I* growl when I'm pleased, and wag my tail when I'm angry. Therefore I'm mad.'

'*I* call it purring, not growling,' said Alice.

'Call it what you like,' said the Cat. 'Do you play croquet with the Queen today?'

'I should like it very much,' said Alice, 'but I haven't been invited yet.'

'You'll see me there,' said the Cat, and vanished.

Alice was not much surprised at this, she was getting so well used to queer things happening. While she was still looking at the place where it had been, it suddenly appeared again.

'By-the-bye, what became of the baby?' said the Cat. 'I'd nearly forgotten to ask.'

'It turned into a pig,' Alice answered very quietly, just as if the Cat had come back in a natural way.

'I thought it would,' said the Cat, and vanished again.

Alice waited a little, half expecting to see it again, but it did not appear, and after a minute or two she walked on in the direction in which the March Hare was said to live. 'I've seen hatters before,' she said to herself: 'the March Hare will be much the most interesting, and perhaps, as

this is May, it won't be raving mad – at least not so mad as it was in March.' As she said this, she looked up, and there was the Cat again, sitting on a branch of a tree.

'Did you say "pig", or "fig"?' said the Cat.

'I said "pig",' replied Alice: 'and I wish you wouldn't

keep appearing and vanishing so suddenly: you make one quite giddy!'

'All right,' said the Cat; and this time it vanished quite slowly, beginning with the end of the tail, and ending with the grin, which remained some time after the rest of it had gone.

'Well! I've often seen a cat without a grin,' thought Alice; 'but a grin without a cat! It's the most curious thing I ever saw in all my life!'

The Amethyst Cat

by MARGERY SHARP

EVERYONE knows that in 1860 far too much looting went on at the Summer Palace in Peking. Bric-a-brac carved from jade and crystal proved in particular irresistibly attractive to an acquisitive if not licentious soldiery. (Today, of course, such objects would probably be described as having been liberated.) The result was the dispersal through Western Europe of a great number of miniature Chinese masterpieces; and Sherrard, some hundred years later, thought he had his eye on one of them.

Sherrard looked through the plate glass window at the cat, and the cat, or so it seemed, looked back through the window at Sherrard.

It was a portly and sagacious creature; couchant in an attitude of great comfort and dignity; about nine inches long by five high, carved from a block of amethyst quartz which must thus have been considerably larger. The body was light grey, striated with crystal, the mask and ears violet – almost Siamese colouring; but the broad complacent face, sunk so reposefully upon the broad chest, had nothing of a Siamese's nervous tension. It was a Chinese cat – and, in Sherrard's opinion, a masterpiece.

Sherrard at this juncture, it so happened, greatly desired to make a gift of surpassing beauty to a young Chinese lady, resident in New York. He therefore entered the shop, and a moment or two later balanced the creature on his palm.

He could just manage it. For its size, it was astonishingly heavy. It must have weighed about seven pounds. It was also astonishingly cold – like wet ice.

'Amethyst quartz?' suggested Sherrard.

'Amethyst quartz,' agreed the proprietress, with a polite smile for her customer's knowledgeableness. She was a small, elegant woman, thus matching her establishment, which was situated in Piccadilly; for his pocket's sake Sherrard would have preferred less *chic*, but at the same time recognized that one couldn't expect such a cat to turn up in – to put up with – any flea-market. 'Of the finest quality,' added the proprietress. 'So is the workmanship. Turn him over.'

Sherrard obeyed. The cat's underside was as exquisitely carved as the rest of him: four delicate paws, the claws withdrawn, were tucked neatly into a comfortable belly. Near the root of the tail Sherrard made out a small, faintly-incised Chinese ideogram.

'Have you its pedigree?' inquired Sherrard, without irony.

The proprietress shrugged.

'Chinese and, say, eighteenth century. Not that I'm an expert. I bought it at a sale in a country house, because I was lucky, there were no Chinese experts there. And, of course, I know what my eyes tell me, it's the work of a considerable artist.'

Sherrard's eyes told him the same thing. He appreciated it, it gave him confidence, that she didn't produce any tale of loot from the Summer Palace to put the price up. In any case, the price was quite high enough for Sherrard.

'Two hundred pounds,' murmured the proprietress indifferently.

'I'll have to think,' said Sherrard. 'May I let you know tomorrow?'

Indeed he had to think. He was a foreign correspondent, and a successful, even a celebrated one; on his pay and expenses he lived a thoroughly ample life; but to put down two hundred pounds cash – six hundred dollars, two hundred thousand francs, three hundred and fifty thousand lire – wasn't a trifle to him. All the rest of that day, and well into the night, he mulled it over.

There were several reasons why he wished to make Maria in New York some exquisitely beautiful gift. In the first place she was herself exquisitely beautiful, and like to like. (Her Chinese name meant Small Pink Lotus Bud at Dawn, and it suited her. Maria discarded it to become Maria when she so thankfully and enthusiastically became an American citizen.) Had he been a millionaire, and had he known nothing of Maria but her appearance, Sherrard would have bought her the amethyst cat as a mere matter of artistic propriety. But he did, besides, know her, he'd known her off and on for some years, and had the greatest admiration for her character also. Educated in China, at a Quaker school, sent on a scholarship to an American university, it perhaps hadn't been difficult for Maria herself to acquire citizenship in the New World; but with incredible pains and persistence, as soon as she could support a dependant, she succeeded in bringing over her only living relative – an uncle so old and so useless that only a heart of gold could see him as anything but a burden. 'He was kind to me when I was little,' said Maria, 'and I've got him off opium on to Coca-Cola!'

For as well as being golden-hearted and beautiful, she was sensible and strong-minded. She had every feminine quality. Every time he left New York without asking her to marry him, Sherrard regretted it in the plane.

Why he didn't ask her to marry him was partly because he was so used to being a bachelor, and partly because Maria kept him always, very slightly, at a distance. She kept everyone, Sherrard fancied, slightly at a distance. In the hospital where she worked as a masseuse she had dozens of friends, but no intimates; as she had dozens of escorts, but no one particular escort. Her reserve was like a delicate Chinese fan fluttering perpetually before her face, which she couldn't cast aside even though she wanted to. Sherrard thought that at the sight of the amethyst cat – so surpassingly beautiful, expensive and Chinese – perhaps that fan would for an instant drop; never, if he seized his chance, to be picked up again . . .

He went back to the shop next day, and wrote out a cheque.

Sherrard had known all along that he was buying no common cat; the personality it developed, on the flight out to New York, was none the less disconcerting. It created difficulties, and attracted attention, all the way.

To begin with, he hadn't cared to pack it in his luggage. It was too precious, and possibly too fragile. (It might have survived at least a century of racketing about, and perhaps a century before that; Sherrard still thought of it as fragile, because precious.) So he stuffed it into his overnight bag, where its weight, on the airport scales, produced a startled query from the officer in charge. 'It's a cat,' said Sherrard shortly. 'I've a cat in my bag.' Someone to the rear laughed, but the officer looked grim. 'Livestock?' he inquired sternly. 'No, quartz,' snapped Sherrard. He pulled it out; the officer grinned and passed him – on payment of excess; and as they were immediately marshalled to their plane, Sherrard boarded it with the cat under his arm.

Unusually, the seat beside him remained vacant. Having dumped the cat down on it, he left it there. The cat settled down very comfortably but continued to attract attention. Sherrard was reminded of the one and only flight he'd made with his Aunt Gertrude – a charming and sociable old lady who'd apparently regarded the whole trip as a nice At Home given by the airline. Like his Aunt Gertrude (which was something), the cat made contact only with the nicest people; chiefly elderly ladies travelling with their husbands. One such couple – whom Sherrard mentally christened The Texans, on no other grounds than the man's broad-brimmed hat and general air of prosperity – sat directly across the aisle; the lady in particular was perfectly charmed by the cat and the cat, it couldn't be denied, appeared most complacently to receive her attentions. It didn't purr, it couldn't, but it appeared to purr. Finally Sherrard, who unlike Aunt Gertrude felt no social obligations whatever, covered it over with his scarf.

He was none the less roused from sleep, shortly before arrival, by the Texan.

'Pardon me, I thought you were awake,' the Texan apologized.

'At least I should be,' said Sherrard – his Aunt Gertrude, as it were reminding him of his manners.

'The fact is, my wife's taken a remarkable fancy to your cat. If I could get one similar for her, I'd be very glad to know where to go for it.'

'I'm sorry, I'm afraid this one's about two hundred years old,' said Sherrard.

The Texan looked at it respectfully. (Somehow, during the night, it had got its head out again.)

'You mean no one makes them nowadays?'

'Not that I know of,' said Sherrard.

'Too bad,' said the Texan regretfully. 'All the same, I'd like you to take my card – just to show Maisie I'm trying. If you ever run across another, and have the kindness to let me know, I'll be deeply obliged.'

Sherrard pocketed the bit of pasteboard and tried to doze off again. But he'd been disturbed, for a man of his fifty years, too thoroughly; instead he sat and thought about Maria.

The cat dozed off all right. Sherrard didn't remember pulling the scarf over its head a second time, but when he looked again, not an ear showed. It was thus in fine fettle to make an exhibition of itself at the customs; but, leaning on its age, carried Sherrard through without difficulty.

Sherrard reached Maria's flat about seven that evening. There were several professional contacts he had needed to make first; he'd had no time to get the cat wrapped, as he'd thought of doing, in some elegant packing. It was still simply muffled in his scarf. But as he set it down so muffled, on the little table in the centre of her living room, it presented at least an intriguing shape.

Maria was there waiting for him. He'd cabled her. Actually he'd cabled her twice – once from London, once from Gander.

'You are the nicest friend in the world!' cried Maria. There was still, even in the pretty, affectionate phrase, a formality: as though she offered a little poem of welcome brushed across a fan. She stood before him none the less so exquisitely beautiful, so explicitly friendly, that his heart rose. 'And you've brought me a present from England!' cried Maria. 'Really, you're too good!'

Smiling and eager, she poked at the bundle with a tentative forefinger. It was another of her charming traits that she was readily pleased, and always showed her pleasure; yet Sherrard had no doubt that she reserved pleasure still in store, so to speak, that she would find the unimaginably right words of gratitude and admiration, when she saw his marvellous gift, that before the cat, her compatriot, in short, the fan of reserve would at last drop.

Already she was more eager, more caught up by a flow of pleasure and excitement, than he had ever seen her.

'Do I unwrap it, or do you show it me?' demanded Maria. 'I'm not going to guess, I'm too impatient!'

'Sit down, and I'll put it in your lap,' said Sherrard.

Obediently, Maria sat. She even (to give *him* pleasure) closed her eyes – and this momentarily distracted Sherrard, for he had never before seen Maria with her eyes shut. She looked at once ageless, and very young; her lids were the colour of tea-roses; and with irrational tenderness Sherrard realized that her lashes weren't long, as he'd always believed them to be, but quite short and scrubby, like little brushes . . .

'What are you waiting for?' urged Maria.

Sherrard pulled the cat out of its wrapping and set

it down on her knee, between her slim welcoming hands.

For an instant, undoubtedly, as she opened her eyes, the fan dropped. But only for an instant. Almost immediately her features recomposed themselves into an expression of extreme politeness.

'How perfectly *lovely*,' said Maria.

Sherrard picked up the table-lamp and held it so that the light shone down through the violet ears.

'It's amethyst quartz.'

'I see it is. Lovely!' repeated Maria. With quick, intelligent fingers, she traced the curve from nape to tail, tipped the cat over, scrutinized its underneath, and settled it back between her palms.

'Oh, dear, I hope you didn't pay too much for it!' cried Maria uncontrollably . . .

Then Sherrard knew that the emotion she'd so briefly betrayed had indeed been what he'd fancied it. For a moment, incredulously, he'd fancied she was disappointed. Now he knew she was.

'Does that mean it's no good?'

'Of course not! It's beautiful! Only if they told you it was eighteenth century, you might have paid four or five hundred dollars.'

Sherrard was very quick-witted. He saw what was coming and got in first.

'Of course it's only a modern reproduction.'

Maria smiled with relief.

'I'm so glad you weren't robbed – as people can be, quite shockingly! Now I can enjoy my present with a good conscience!'

She jumped up, and set the cat first on the table again, then on a tabouret, then on the mantelpiece, seeking where it would look best; she gaily and charmingly made a fuss of it, even giving it a vase of violets to smell at, a little silver box to play with. Nothing could have been prettier; but Sherrard remained unhappy. He was indeed in a most distressing quandary; the sheer costliness of the gift had been a large part of its point – a declaration, so to speak, of his intentions; yet he couldn't now admit to it without also admitting himself a sucker – worse, without bringing down on his head Maria's mingled sympathy and exasperation. She had always an acute dislike of any kind of waste – in her early days in America Sherrard recalled how she'd worried over the crusts cut off from sandwiches – and waste of money ranked next with her to waste of food. She was very nearly parsimonious. Considering her starveling infancy, the trait was a natural one; for the first time Sherrard found himself disliking it. He hadn't toted the cat halfway round the world to have its price asked! True, Maria hadn't done so yet, in so many words, but Sherrard strongly suspected her of wanting to, certain of finding it exorbitant in any case . . .

He also suspected – too late, too late! – that she didn't much care for the cat at all.

'Next time I'll bring you a cashmere twin-set,' said he.

Undeniably, her eyes sparkled.

'Will you really? I'll give you my size.'

It didn't soothe Sherrard's soreness that the cat meanwhile continued to sit handsome and complacent as ever, looking every minute of two hundred years old. It met Sherrard's gaze affably. 'All right, so you fooled me,' thought Sherrard. (It didn't, oddly enough, occur to him that he might have been fooled by the shopkeeper; he was convinced that the cat had fooled them both.) 'But now you've run into an expert,' thought Sherrard nastily, 'and as soon as I'm out of town you'll be put in your proper place . . . which is probably the back of a clothes-closet.'

Naturally the cat's expression didn't alter. Maria exclaimed afresh, that very moment, at its air of aplomb. Sherrard gave the impostor another dirty look, for his own aplomb left much to be desired – he having not realized the

implications of his hasty threat. '*As soon as I'm out of town,*' he'd warned the cat; did he then mean to leave cat and Maria together behind him? Wasn't he after all going to ask Maria to be his wife? And if not, why not? Because she'd wanted to know how much he'd paid for her present? Put so, the thing was ridiculous; there stood Maria just as exquisite as he remembered her, just as charmingly affectionate, having moreover, and at last, dropped the fan of her reserve – to reveal behind it the admirable wifely quality of concern for a man's pocket . . .

What an admirable wife she would make!

She'd probably run a wonderfully economical kitchen.

Not impossibly, when he wanted to go out on the town, she'd have something in the oven.

She'd certainly want to see any dinner-bill.

Sherrard glanced again at the amethyst cat, and the cat

with ancient wisdom gazed back at Sherrard. (With *fictitiously* ancient wisdom, Sherrard reminded himself.) It was shocking, and it was completely out of period, that the cat appeared to murmur something under its whiskers about wives to keep men steady, but concubines to keep them young. For a moment Sherrard felt he should absolutely apologize to Maria for the cat's immorality; but on second thoughts recognized that to her a lump of quartz, however masterly carved, remained simply a lump of quartz.

Which brought him to another point. Beautiful Maria – sensible and kind Maria – lacked imagination. 'And what else do I deal in?' Sherrard asked himself. 'I, the factual reporter, what else after all do I deal in? Don't I produce, for those who haven't the wit or opportunity to make them for themselves, the images of President, Prime Minister, statesman? Don't I image the whole world, or try to, in a column of print? Maybe it would be all right for me, maybe it would be even good for me, to marry a wife with no imagination at all; but somehow I don't think so . . .'

Complacently upon Maria's mantelpiece sat the amethyst cat.

Sherrard turned back to Maria. He didn't know how long the silence had lasted, only that it had lasted quite long enough. 'Where would you like to go for dinner?' he asked uneasily.

Now Maria, damn it, was looking uneasily at *him*.

'My dear, I hate to tell you,' she apologized, 'but actually I've a date already. And it's one I can't put off – with a boy from China, a boy who knew my family there . . . It's his first evening in New York, you see, without me he won't know what to do with himself. You do understand, don't you?'

'Perfectly,' said Sherrard. 'You'll see he isn't robbed.'

Maria laughed in happy relief.

'That among other things! Though tonight I think he wants to be rather grand and extravagant, to celebrate *getting* here!'

'Just for once I don't suppose it matters,' suggested Sherrard, 'if you keep him on a tight rein afterwards?'

'Oh, I mean to,' agreed Maria seriously. (No wonder the cat looked smug. 'That's the sort of lad for *her*,' it seemed to say, 'a lad she can boss about; see what I've saved you from!' Sherrard ignored the brute.) 'So I really ought to dress up a little,' added Maria, now glancing frankly at the clock, 'but won't you wait and meet him? He is studying medicine, and he seems to be really quite brilliant ... Please wait!'

'If you want me to, of course I will,' said Sherrard amiably.

He felt suddenly flat – flat and sore. He wasn't yet grateful to the cat at all. He felt let down. For nothing had turned out as he'd planned; even his own emotions had gone adrift, he didn't even feel jealous of the boy from China; and it wasn't exactly Maria's fault, so that he couldn't even feel angry with Maria. His anger turned itself upon the cat – upon the smug impostor he'd toted half round the world, with no other result than to put himself, Sherrard, in danger of looking a fool . . .

'What's the Chinese name that means Labour-in-Vain?' Sherrard mentally inquired of the amethyst cat. 'You should know; it's yours.'

He had been alone perhaps five minutes (while Maria dressed up) when the door discreetly opened. The old party who now joined him, however, was in appearance at least less discreet than showy. Maria's efforts to turn her uncle into a hundred-per-cent American had in one respect succeeded only too well: he wore a Palm Beach shirt. There were hibiscus blossoms upon it, also sea-horses, also bathing-beauties, but above its brilliant uninhibited colouring a face like an old walnut peered, incongruously diffident, humble and submissive.

'I beg pardon,' murmured Maria's uncle. 'I did not know anyone was present . . .'

'Don't go, come on in and keep me company,'

said Sherrard. 'I'm just waiting to vet Maria's new beau.'

It was as incongruous to him, that slangy turn of phrase, as was the Palm Beach shirt on Maria's uncle. Sherrard recognized it at once, recognizing also that he wasn't quite himself. Fortunately the old man, it seemed, recognized nothing but a permission to enter; he sidled in bowing politely, with a smile that revealed a really splendid set of false teeth. Sherrard was again aware of an incongruity: they were so wonderfully confident, those splendid American dentures, yet the old man's smile remained humble . . .

'Your company will give me great pleasure,' Sherrard corrected himself. 'Perhaps you remember me? My name is Sherrard.'

Extraordinarily, to this overture there was no response at all.

The old man mightn't even have heard. It was extraordinary indeed – one moment all his attention was fixed on Sherrard, the next it had flown away; one moment his eyes dropped humbly before the stranger, the next they were riveted on the mantelpiece. With short, hasty steps he almost trotted across the room; pushed his wrinkled old face against the smooth complacent countenance of the cat, laid his fingers (like a bundle of bamboo twigs) to the curve of the cat's nape, tipped the beast over, scrutinized its belly – and only then turned back to Sherrard.

Maria had always insisted on her uncle speaking correct English, so that he could never say anything very quickly; but the words got out at last. 'How – came – this – object – here?'

'I brought it to give Maria,' said Sherrard. 'D'you like it?'

'I *made* it!' proclaimed Maria's uncle triumphantly. 'See, under my mark!'

There was now naturally much Sherrard understood that he hadn't before. His thoughts raced. Poor Maria, to begin with! – had she recognized her uncle's mark too, or only his general style? Or even remembered, perhaps, sitting under his work-bench as he chipped and polished and engraved at that very beast? In whichever case, what a facer for her, what a grotesquely absurd disappointment! And how well, in the circumstances, she'd behaved! Sherrard felt all his affection for her flooding back – not too strongly, not strongly enough to make him jealous of her Chinese beau – but with sufficient warmth to heal all soreness. 'Poor Maria, it's a wonder she didn't box my ears!' thought Sherrard – and began to laugh.

Maria's uncle had been laughing for some time. He stood and rocked with silent, delighted laughter, the cat clasped to his bosom, all humility wiped from his face by an artist's giddy pride. Even his teeth looked very nearly natural.

'Listen,' said Sherrard, 'I'm taking that cat away from Maria and giving it to you. *Back* to you. You understand? It's yours. If you want to sell, I can give you an address where they'll probably pay anything you like to ask for it. And if you can lay hands on any more quartz, or whatever else you carve cats out of, I imagine you've a very rewarding future. I see I'll have to say all this over again,' concluded Sherrard, 'so in the meantime, instead of waiting for Maria's wonderboy, why shouldn't we go out to dinner ourselves?'

There was a response, all right, then. Half incredulous, half eager, like a very old tortoise sniffing the spring, Maria's uncle poked forth his head above the cat's. 'You and I go out to *dinner*?'

'Why not?' said Sherrard.

'Chinese style?'

'Why not? We needn't,' added Sherrard, as the old man appeared to turn something over in his mind, 'disturb Maria. We'll just leave her a note.'

But it wasn't Maria the old man was thinking of. Stroking a finger down the cat, nose to tail. 'You are certain,' he pressed, 'it can be sold for much? For how much? A – hundred dollars?'

'Six hundred,' said Sherrard – justifiably confident in his Texan.

Every tooth in the old head gleamed anew.

'Then *you* shall be *my* guest, not I yours,' pronounced Maria's uncle.

What an evening it was!

All the best dinners, Sherrard remembered once hearing, are eaten on credit; the old man's credit with a certain compatriot restaurateur appeared illimitable – especially after he had displayed the amethyst cat, which they bore with them. (It didn't even have to suffer the indignity of being left in pawn.) They dined, with intervals for conversation, while special dishes were being cooked, or special delicacies sent for, until well past midnight. Sherrard was rather queasy next day and so, as reported by Maria, was her uncle. 'Where did you two go for heaven's sake?' demanded Maria, over the telephone. 'And why didn't you stay to meet Harry? We were disappointed.'

'Didn't you and Harry have a good time too?' asked Sherrard.

'Yes, of course we did,' said Maria. 'We had a wonderful time; we ate steak. But my uncle tells me you've given him my cat, he says now it's his!'

'As you always knew it was,' said Sherrard.

There was a slight pause. Then to his immense satisfaction – what a splendid girl she was! – he heard Maria giggle. 'How could I tell you? But really it's the nicest thing that ever happened, my uncle is so pleased! And what do you think he means to do *now*?'

'I know; we spent last night planning it,' said Sherrard. 'He is going to go back to carving cats, and make hundreds of dollars and put them all away in a box and write on it, "*For Maria's Dowry*' . . .'

Sherrard himself boarded the east-bound plane as usual unwed – or affianced – but not unhappy either. He hadn't even the amethyst cat with him; but both felt better off as they were, and at least it made for a peaceful journey. He was indeed two hundred pounds to the bad, which he could ill afford; but there had been something to show for it. An old man's face of bliss, as he looked down at his no longer useless hands: an old man's joy in dowering the kind child who'd succoured him . . .

'Cheap at the price,' thought Sherrard; glared disagreeably at his neighbours, in case any should be minded to address him, and went to sleep.

The Cats

by Jan Struther

In Sycamore Square
At the crack of dawn
The white cats play
On the grey-green lawn;
One is the owner
Of Number Three
And the other pretends
To belong to me.
Slowly over
The dew-soaked grass
Their low tense bodies
Like serpents pass
And each imperceptible
Smooth advance
Is an intricate step
In a mystic dance,
Which ends in the cat
From Number Three
Rushing quite suddenly
Up a tree,
While mine walks off
With a dignified air
To the other end
of Sycamore Square
But nobody yet has ever found out
What in the world
The game's about.

The Soul of a Cat

by MARGARET BENSON

PERSIS was a dainty lady, pure Persian, blue and white, silky haired. When this story opens she was in middle age, the crisis of her life had passed. She had had kittens, she had seen them grow up, and as they grew she had grown to hate them, with a hatred founded on jealousy and love. She was a cat of extreme sensibility, of passionate temper, of a character attractive and lovable from its very intensity. We had been forced to face Persis' difficulty with her and make our choice – should we let her go about with a sullen face to the world, green eyes glooming wretchedly upon it, an intensity of wretchedness, jealousy and hate consuming her little cat's heart, or would we follow Persis' wishes about the kittens, and give them up, when they grew to be a burden on her mind and heart? For while they were young she loved them much. She chose favourites among them, usually the one most like herself, lavished a wealth of care, with anxiety in a small, troubled, motherly face, on their manners, their appearance, their amusements.

I remember one pathetic scene on a rainy evening in late summer, when the kittens of the time were playing about the room, and Persis came in wet and draggled with something in her mouth. We thought it was a dead bird, and though regretting the fact, did not hinder her when she deposited it before her favourite kitten, a shy, grey creature, and retired to the lap of a forbearing friend to make her toilet. But while she was thus engaged we saw that the thing she had brought in was a shivering little bird, a belated fledgling, alive and unhurt. The grey kitten had not touched it, but with paws tucked under him was regarding it with a cold, steady gaze. He was quite unmoved when we took it away and restored it to a profitless liberty, with a few scathing remarks on the cruelty of cats. It was so nice and affectionate of a father to initiate his little son into the pleasures of sport and show him how to play a fish, but quite another thing for a brutal cat to show her kitten how to play with a live bird – a cat, indeed, from whom we should have expected a sympathetic imagination!

When Persis had washed and combed herself she came down to see how her son was enjoying his first attempt at sport; but no affectionate father sympathizing with his boy for losing his fish would have been half so much distressed as Persis to find her kitten robbed of his game. She ran round the room crying as she went, searched for the bird under chairs and tables, sprang on the knees of her friends to seek it, and wailed for the loss of her present to her son.

Again, there was no danger that she would not face in defence of her kittens. My brother had a wire-haired terrier of horrid reputation as a cat-killer. The name of the terrier, for an occult and complicated reason, was Two-Timothy-Three-Ten, but it was generally abbreviated. Tim, large and formidable even to those who had not heard of his exploits, slipped into the room once where a placid domestic scene was in process. Without a moment's pause the cat was on him like a wild beast. I caught Timothy and held him up, but the cat had dug her claws so firmly into his foot that she, too, was lifted off the ground.

But as the kittens grew older, maternal tenderness and delights faded, maternal cares ceased, and a dull, jealous misery settled down over Persis. She had been left down in the country with a kitten once – alas! a tabby kitten – which was growing old enough to leave her when I came over for the day and went to see her. The kitten, unconscious of his unfortunate appearance, was as happy as most kittens; he walked round the cat and did not mind an occasional growl or cuff. But she, not responding at all to my caresses, sat staring out before her with such black, immovable despair on her face that I shall not easily forget it.

Thus the cat's life was a series of violent changes of mood.

While her kittens were young she was blissful with them, trustful to all human beings; as they grew older she became sullen, suspicious, and filled with jealous gloom. When they were gone she again became affectionate and gentle; she decked herself with faded graces, was busied with secret errands, and intent on aesthetic pleasure – the smell of fresh air, each particular scent of ivy leaves round the trunk of the cedar.

She caught influenza once in an interval of peace and came near dying, and, they said, received attention seriously and gratefully like a sick person; I was not surprised to hear that her friend sacrificed a pet bantam to tempt the returning appetite of the invalid.

While we were homeless for a year or more, Persis was lodged at the old home farm, and lorded it over the animals. Two cats were there: one the revered and hideous Tom, with whose white hair Persis had bestrewn a room in a fit of passion. He had left the house at once for the farm and wisely refused to return. Now he was a prop of the establishment. He killed the rats, he sat serene in the sun, was able to ignore the village dogs and cuff the boisterous collie puppies of the farm. So he met Persis on secure and dignified terms. It was well, for he had formed a tender attachment to her daughter; they drank milk out of a saucer together, looking like the Princess and the Ploughboy; and when the Ploughboy went out hunting (for he must vary his diet a little – unmitigated rat is monotonous) he invariably brought back the hind legs of the rabbit for the Princess.

Strange to say, the Princess was the only one of the grown-up kittens with whom Persis entered into terms of friendship; so while the Princess ate the rabbits of the Ploughboy, Persis ate the sparrows provided by the Princess, and they were all at peace.

She rejoined us again when we settled in a country town. The house was backed by a walled garden; exits and entrances were easier than in the larger houses where Persis had lived with us before. She loved to get up by the wistaria, climb across the conservatory roof, and get in and out through bedroom windows. She found a black grandson already established, it is true, but in a strictly subordinate position. Justice was cast to the – cats, and they fought it out between them; and when Persis threw herself into the fray there could be but one end. Ra liked comfort, but his sensibilities were undeveloped. If he could get the food he desired (and he invariably entered the room with fish or pheasant) he did not care how or where it was given him; a plate of fish-bones in the conservatory would be more grateful than a stalled ox under his grandmother's eye. But to the old cat the attention was everything; she took the food not so much because she cared for it as because it was offered individually to her. If Ra managed to establish himself on the arm of a chair he would remind the owner of his desires by the tap of a black paw, or by gently intercepting a fork. But Persis' sole desire was that she might be desired; the invitation was the great point, not the feast; she lay purring with soft, intelligent eyes, which grew hard and angry if the form of her dusky grandson appeared in the open door. She would get down from the lap on which she was lying, strike at the hand which tried to detain her, and – but by this time Ra had been removed and peace restored.

Her most blissful moments were when she could find her mistress in bed, and curl up beside her, pouring out a volume of soft sound, or when she was shown to company. Then she walked with dainty steps and waving tail as in the old days, with something of the same grace, though not with the old beauty, trampling a visitor's dress with rhythmically moving paws, and the graciously modest air of one who confers an honour. It came near to pathos to see her play the great lady and the petted kitten before the vet who came to prescribe for her. Now she was all gratitude for attentions, and whereas when she was young she would not come to a call out of doors, but coquetted with us just beyond our reach, now she would come running in from the garden when I called her, loved to be taken up and lie with chin and paws resting on my shoulder, looking down from it like a child. The old nurse carried her on one arm like a baby, and the cat stretched out paws on each side round her waist.

She had more confidence in human dealings, too. I had to punish her once, to her great surprise. She ran a few steps and waited for me with such confidence that it was difficult to follow up the punishment, more especially as Taffy watched exultant, and came up smiling to insist on the fact that he was a good dog.

Taffy's relationship with the cat was anything but cordial. It was her fault, for he had well learnt the household maxim 'cats first and pleasure afterwards'. But Persis can hardly be said to have treated him like a lady; she did not actually show fight, but vented ill-temper by pushing rudely in front of him with a disagreeable remark as she passed.

All this time Persis was growing old and small. Her coat was thick, but shorter than of old; her tail waved far less wealth of hair. She jumped into the fountain one day by mistake, and as she stood still, with clinging hair, under the double shock of the water and the laughter, one noticed what a little shrunken cat she had become; only her face was young and vivid with conflicting passion.

Then the last change of her life came. We went to a place which was a paradise for cats, but a paradise ringed with death; a rambling Elizabethan house, where mice ran and rattled behind the panels; a garden with bushes to creep behind and strange country creatures stirring in the grass; barns which were a preserve for rats and mice; and finally the three most important elements of happiness, entire freedom, no smuts, and no grandson.

Persis was overwhelmed with pressure of affairs; one saw her crouching near the farm in early morning; met her later on the stairs carrying home game, and was greeted only by a quick look as of one intent on business.

The one drawback to this place was that it was surrounded by woods, carefully preserved.

By this time I had come to two clear resolves; the first, that I would never again develop the sensibilities of an animal beyond certain limits; for one creates claims that one has no power to satisfy. The feelings of a sensitive animal are beyond our control, and beyond its own also.

And the second was this; since it is impossible to let an animal when it is old and ill live among human beings as it may when it is healthy; since it can by no possibility understand why sympathy is denied it and demonstrations of affection checked; I would myself, as soon as such signs of broken intercourse occurred, give Persis the lethal water. I had been haunted by the pathos in the face of a dog who had been and indeed still was a family pet; but he was deaf. Even when he was fondled an indescribable depression hung about him; he had fallen into silence, he knew not how or why. Dogs respond to nothing more quickly than the tones of the human voice, but now no voice came through the stillness. Despairingly he put himself, as they told us, in the way of those who passed, lay on steps or in the doorways. Since we cannot find means to alleviate such sufferings we can at least end them.

But I never needed to put this determination into effect. The last time I saw Persis was once when she came to greet me at the door, and lifting her I noticed how light she was; and again I saw her coming downstairs on some business of her own, with an air at once furtive and arrogant, quaint in so small a creature.

Then Persis vanished.

She had been absent before for days at a time; had once disappeared for three weeks and returned thin and exhausted. So at first we did not trouble; then we called her in the garden, in the fields and the coverts, wrote to find out if she had returned to some old home, and offered a reward for her finding; but all was fruitless. I do not know now whether she had gone away as some creatures do, to die alone, for the signs of age were on her; or if she had met a speedy death at the hands of a gamekeeper while she was following up some wild romance of the woods.

So vanished secretly from life that strange, troubled little soul of a cat – a troubled soul, for it was not the animal loves and hates which were too much for her (these she had ample spirit and courage to endure) but she knew a jealous love for beings beyond her dim power of comprehension, a passionate desire for praise and admiration from creatures whom she did not understand, and these waked a strange conflict and turmoil in the vivid and limited nature, troubling her relations with her kind, filling her now with black despairs, and painful passions, and now with serene, half understood content.

Who shall say whether a creature like this can ever utterly perish? How shall we who know so little of their nature profess to know so much of their future?

Minna Minna Mowbray

by MICHAEL JOSEPH

AMONG all my cats, past and present, Minna Minna Mowbray was an outstanding personality. Except to a connoisseur of cats Minna was not physically impressive. She was a short-haired tortoiseshell tabby, with tiny white paws to match her piquant white face. Her head was small but beautifully shaped. The rather large ears were grey, and streaks of orange fur ran down between her amber eyes and on either side to the under part of her delicate jaw, forming a regularly designed tortoiseshell frame for her white face. A flash of coral pink was visible when she opened her dainty mouth. Her teeth were white and strong. The under part of her body was pure white and even in the soot and grime of London this was nearly always spotlessly clean. At kitten time it was dazzlingly white. This part of her was domestically known as her 'ermine'. When she was feeling particularly sociable, certain favoured members of the household were permitted, sometimes even encouraged, to massage it gently.

Minna was small, as cats go, but exquisitely proportioned. All her movements were graceful. She would sit upright, with her tiny forepaws close together, her long, rather full tail coiled round. Her favourite position for sleep was a crouch, the hind legs drawn up close and head resting on the outstretched forepaws which she converted into cushions by turning them inwards. Sometimes she preferred to lie on her side, legs outstretched luxuriously at queer angles. Various attitudes I learned to recognize as meditative (often assumed, this one), ecstatic, proud (both these when kittens were on view), majestically indignant (accompanied by business with tail), inquiring (as when she wanted to know what I was eating – this was primarily curiosity, for as often as not she rejected after close scrutiny the morsel I offered her) and leave-me-alone-please. This last was indicated by a haughty turning aside of her head; if this failed she would calmly turn her back and if *that* gesture had no effect she would walk off with the air of an offended dowager.

Like her mother, Lady Dudley, she had no voice, her vocal chord being partially paralysed. Oddly enough – for such a physical defect is presumably not hereditary – her kittens seldom cried, except when they were very young. Minna opened her mouth when, for instance, she wanted a door open, but no sound emerged. When she was greatly agitated about something a faint squeak was audible if you listened carefully. She could purr loudly enough but did not purr often. She could also swear, in delicate but determined fashion, but this again was reserved for special occasions.

Minna Minna Mowbray was a gentle cat. She never attempted to scratch a human. Babies and small boys could do what they liked with her. Like all self-respecting cats she disliked rough handling but she never attempted retaliation. If her tail were pulled or her long, sensitive whiskers touched she showed displeasure by asking silently to be allowed to go.

Contrary to expert advice, Minna wore a collar – an elegant green collar with an identity disc and two brass bells. A collar, I have heard, is undesirable because it may catch in the spikes of railings or the branches of a tree, but in my experience this risk is negligible if a cat is trained to a collar when very young. It is possible that a grown cat may so resent the introduction of a collar that he will try to drag it off and thereby injure himself, but I have never heard of an instance.

Minna was proud of her collar and plainly enjoyed wearing it. She put the bells to practical use, whenever she wanted to be admitted to a room, by shaking her head outside the closed door. She never worried if she were late for breakfast, knowing that the tinkle of her bell would cause the door to be opened. Sometimes when she rang outside the door I delayed, for the satisfaction of hearing her tinkle imperiously repeated. And with what an air of affronted majesty she stalked into the room if she had been thus kept waiting! Custom brought her to the dining room at breakfast time, not hunger, for as often as not she turned up her aristocratic nose at the fish or milk offered her.

Minna also learned to summon her kittens by sounding her bells. When the babies got to the exploring stage and escaped from the maternal eye in house or garden Minna recalled them by an agitated peal. They usually answered the summons promptly but Minna would continue to ring until they did.

Minna could silence her bell as effectively as she could ring it. Not a sound was to be heard when she stalked a bird. What a waste of time it is to 'bell the cat' with the intention of suppressing natural instincts!

The real owner of my house in those days was Minna. She walked about with the manner of a landed proprietor surveying his domain; on the whole proud, but reserving the right to be critical. The day nursery and the kitchen were her favourite rooms. The dining room and what my family insisted on calling 'the study' were frequently patronized. Her appearances in the other rooms were rare, with the exception of my bedroom in the winter, when warm milk was usually to be coaxed from me last thing at night.

When she was younger the bathroom enchanted her. She soon discovered it to be a magic, fascinating and deliciously dangerous place with a queer contraption which was often filled with water. As a kitten, Minna used to insist on stalking round the edge of the bath when there was water in it, balancing precariously at the rounded corners. Running water fascinated her and she would play with a dripping tap for hours. Her mother, and some of Minna's own kittens, shared this fondness for running water: and so did my favourite Siamese, Charles. Micky Jos, one of Minna's most spirited kittens, had a passion for water and thoroughly enjoyed being soaked to the skin. But when she was grown up, with matronly responsibilities, Minna seldom played with water. It was beneath her dignity.

Another forsaken attraction in her middle age was the piano. As a kitten she took a great interest in it. As soon as it was opened she would jump on the keyboard. A series of spirited discords marked her progress from bass to treble and back again. She much preferred the bass, possibly because the deeper volume of sound or the stronger vibration took her fancy. But as she grew up Minna tired of the piano and took no notice of it.

Minna had a curious aversion to whistling. If I tried to whistle (it is not one of my accomplishments) Minna was at once agitated and tried to stop it by putting her paw on my lips. So long as I continued she behaved as one would expect an operatic tenor to behave within hearing of a mouth organ. It was not often that I outraged Minna's artistic susceptibilities, but, when I did, her agitation was intense.

Flowers had a curious attraction for Minna. She could never resist nibbling at them. Spring flowers particularly; if not prevented she would drag daffodils and tulips to the ground for the aesthetic satisfaction of sampling their flavour at her leisure. It was not that she required vegetable diet, for grass, which cats eat regularly when they can get it, was easily accessible. Minna's taste for flowers was not utilitarian.

If there was one thing Minna disliked more than any other it was preparation for a journey. As soon as suitcases were produced she made a prompt and plaintive appearance on the scene. Her agitation always increased when packing began. She would sit mournfully looking on while cupboards and drawers shed their contents, every now and then making a timid and reproachful attempt to interfere with our progress. Even the perfunctory packing of a suitcase for a weekend disturbed her. As for the wholesale removal of the family during the summer, that was a terrible ordeal. On one occasion, when boxes and cases were being brushed as a preliminary to their annual excursion, Minna, shaking her bell in protest, disappeared downstairs, to reappear a few minutes later with Peter, our wire-haired terrier. And then the pair of them sat gazing lugubriously at the signs of departure.

Minna, like most cats, disliked travelling. She had a very commodious basket (I was always annoyed by people who called it a dog basket) and entered it with a poor grace. Poor dear, she knew what was coming. However comfortably the basket was lined, the taxi jolted her up and down and the noise of passing traffic frightened her. The ignominy of being deposited on the platform of a railway station was bad enough, but worse was to follow. The train was the climax of her ordeal.

It was only when Minna was with me in a railway carriage that the sensation of being cooped up in a swiftly-moving box oppressed me. To the more sensitive creature who was my cat the jolting, swaying movement of the small compartment which carried us so swiftly and mysteriously to an unknown destination must have been a paralysing torture. It was only then that I realized how uncomfortable even the most modern railway carriage is. Poor Minna! She would emerge timidly from her basket, grateful for release, but terrified of the unknown. Even in her fear curiosity compelled her to climb for a view of the rushing landscape. A glimpse was enough, and down on to the floor she would spring, crouching and panting, her little tongue hanging from her mouth like a signal of distress.

Only once do I remember Minna facing a railway journey with equanimity – and that, I am sure, was more apparent than real. On that occasion Minna was the proud mother of five kittens, who had also to be transported. The booking-office clerk stared when I told him I had six cats with me. When I added that they were infants in arms and inquired if there were any reduction on account of either age or quantity, or both, he grinned comprehendingly. I was mad, of course. He gave me one ticket and took my half-crown with cheerful tolerance. I betook myself and my cat basket off hastily before he could change his mind.

Minna, evidently determined to conquer her fears for the sake of her kittens, was remarkably self-possessed. She submitted without anxiety to imprisonment in the basket and made no fuss when it was lifted into the taxi and dumped on the floor. Not until the train was speeding southwards and she was allowed the freedom of the carriage did she betray her usual agitation. And then, I observed, only when she was well clear of the basket and its tiny occupants. On the seat beside me, snatching a furtive look out of the window from time to time, Minna went through the familiar performance of crying silently, appealing to me with a troubled paw to bring the dreadful and mysterious train to a standstill. But she had one eye all the time on the basket below and, at the first whimpering sound she was back again, comforting her babies with soft maternal purring.

Minna was always an exemplary mother. But cats vary considerably in this respect. I have already mentioned Meestah, an earlier kitten of Lady Dudley's and therefore a half-sister to Minna. Meestah was worse than neglectful. Her nomenclature, by the way, was based on an Arab word meaning 'to hide', for she had a strange habit of hiding away in odd corners.

It was so long before Meestah became a mother that we began to think she would escape the destiny of female cats, but one day the family arrived – two beautiful kittens. Meestah was most resentful. She would have nothing to do with them. All our coaxing was of no avail. Fortunately this was when I had fourteen cats. About nine of them were females and the kitten problem was rapidly becoming serious. But, luckily for Meestah's kittens, another of my large cat family accommodatingly had kittens just then and as the litter was small we were able to add Meestah's offspring to the new nursery. This was met with the complete approval of both mothers. Meestah was enormously relieved. That was her sole venture into motherhood. How Minna must have disapproved of her!

Minna adored having kittens. Indeed, a cynical friend once remarked that it was her life's work. Her kittens were invariably beautiful and never commonplace. Tortoiseshell tabby, orange, and prettily marked black and white were the usual arrivals, and there were often black flecked with bronze, and kittens mottled distinctively which I am at a loss to describe. Sometimes they were long-haired but usually they inherited the smooth, short-haired coat of their mother. Lest it be thought that I was prejudiced in their favour I must add that Minna's kittens excited admiration even in people usually indifferent to cats.

The fame of my Minna's kittens spread far and wide. Her offspring grew into handsome cats in households all over the country. As my work brought me into touch with a large number of authors, several of her kittens were transferred to literary ownership. Other kittens went to more modest family circles. Our milkman was a regular customer. He had been rather unlucky with his kittens and we cheerfully replaced them. The fishmonger begged for one which captivated him; and the little orange tabby which went to the greengrocer's wife was the recipient of so much affection that I am sure he did not begrudge the others the natural advantages of their respective establishments.

Several times we resolved to keep for ourselves a particularly charming kitten. There was Dinah, a fluffy, sentimental and very attractive young lady whom we brought from the country when we went to live in Regent's Park. I was especially fond of Dinah; whenever Minna held herself aloof – and that was often – Dinah could be depended on to stay purring blissfully on my knee. Dinah was as affectionate as she was decorative.

Not long after our arrival in London Dinah was reported missing. The usual frantic search followed, with no result. Dinah's virtues were magnified with the passing days and, when at last I had to admit there was no longer any hope of finding her, my loss seemed irreparable. I can write of my lost Dinah in this lighthearted way on account of what followed.

One Sunday morning, some weeks later, someone looking out of a window said, 'Isn't that Dinah?' I must explain that the back of our house faced the backs of a crescent of other houses, with small gardens abutting on each other. In these gardens were trees and on a low-lying bough there was a cat. It certainly did look like Dinah.

I ran down to the garden and, climbing on to the wall, made my way along until I was close enough to identify the cat. It *was* Dinah. She watched me coming and when I called her name looked down at me with mild interest. I noticed, with relief, that she had evidently been well fed and cared for. If she recognized me she did not show it. Balancing precariously, I tried to coax her down. Dinah took no notice. So, feeling rather foolish, I retired, in the vain hope that she would follow.

Then I had an inspiration. Dinah might have transferred her affections to another human being, but what about her mother? I dashed into the house, picked up Minna and returned to the garden wall. To reach the tree I had to pass along the tops of several garden walls, on some of which my neighbours had erected trelliswork, wire and such-like impediments. With Minna doing her best to escape it was no easy matter to negotiate these obstacles but, apart from blacking my hands and face and tearing my trousers on a nail, I completed the journey safely. I was confident that Dinah would eagerly come down as soon as she saw Minna; and that Minna would be overjoyed to find her lost baby.

I held Minna up in my arms, balancing on tiptoe, so that the two cats could see each other face to face. Dinah looked down on us with surprise, as if to remark what a strange world this was, with human beings performing antics with other cats on the tops of walls. Her innocent eyes looked at Minna with an expression which clearly said, 'I don't know you, madam, and I don't want to know you.' Minna, on the other hand, recognized her offspring at once. Was she overjoyed? Did she utter the crooning call, half purr, half squeak, with which she had always summoned her kittens? Not she. She spat viciously and began to swear under her breath, in a suppressed note of unmistakable feline hate. She kept it up in a steady crescendo until I lowered her on to the wall and let her go: and then she sprang to the ground, lashing her tail with fury.

At the time I was amazed at this unmotherly behaviour. Dinah was still a kitten and only a few weeks before had been the apple of her mother's eye. It was inconceivable that she could have become a stranger in so short a time. I knew that grown cats fail to recognize their parents, and vice versa, but there was Minna behaving in a way most unnatural and offensive.

Later, I became suspicious. It dawned on me that there was something odd about these disappearances of favourite kittens. Whenever we tried to keep one of a litter, it invariably left us before it was many months old. Everyone who has had anything to do with cats knows how distressed the mother cat is when a kitten is lost or taken away, especially if it is the sole survivor of a litter. Now, it struck me as curious that Minna showed no anxiety when these mysterious departures occurred. We all searched high and low, but Minna was quite unconcerned.

It was when Fowey vanished that my suspicions were confirmed. Fowey (named after the Cornish seaport) was a mischievous orange rascal with china-blue eyes, the throatiest purr I have ever heard, an insatiable appetite and absurd fluffy paws which contrasted oddly with the dainty and aristocratic white feet of his mother. He was an intelligent and charming kitten and everyone made a great fuss of him.

When Fowey was about three months old, Minna took him for long walks. On one occasion I discovered them in a field by the railway a long way from the house. No doubt these expeditions were a source of delight to little Fowey, who wanted to see the world, but there seemed to me to be something sinister about them.

One day mother and son left the house together, Fowey as usual prancing with delight at the prospect of yet another expedition into the fascinating unknown. I watched them go, and there was a queer look in Minna's eye, a look which I can only describe as sinister. Maybe it was only my fancy but it was enough to make me ask at once for Fowey when I returned home that evening. My fears were realized; Minna was there, smirking triumphantly, I fancied, but Fowey was missing.

The days went by and Fowey did not return. We searched in vain. When I asked Minna she looked up at me with an expression so blandly innocent that I am sure she understood perfectly well what I was talking about. Now there is no doubt whatever in my mind that what happened was this. Minna took Fowey to some unfamiliar, deserted spot and there turned round and attacked her unsuspecting offspring. Most probably she said something like this to him:

'Look here, young Fowey (*bang*) you understand this (*scratch*). I'm the only cat wanted in Their house (*biff*) and I'm not (*scratch*) going to have you on the premises. (*Bite, scratch, bang.*) You go and find a home of your own. (*Spit.*) You're not wanted, d'you hear me? (*Bang, spit, bite, scratch, and general fireworks.*)'

No wonder poor Fowey beat a retreat like all the others! He reappeared a few weeks later in one of the gardens at the back; and I discovered that he was lording it over one of the houses in the neighbouring crescent. He had grown into a magnificent cat with a long coat (carefully brushed, I was glad to note) and a huge plume of a tail which I could see daily fluttering in the trees when I was shaving in my bathroom. He was, to judge by appearances, a happy cat and played joyously in the gardens most of the day. But he never came into ours.

Minna was an expert in the art of getting her own way. I can recall only two occasions when she was defeated and then I think she allowed herself to be. The first occasion was the little matter of Peter's basket.

Peter belonged to my wife before I knew her, and, incidentally, there were times when that dog made me feel as a second husband must feel when his wife describes the virtues of his predecessor. Who is this interloper? Peter seemed to say. Well, when Peter became part of the new *ménage* the basket came along too, but in the excitement of meeting Minna Minna Mowbray and the consequent revolution in his habits and ideas of home life, Peter apparently forgot about the basket.

My wife was upset. She said that Peter was so intelligent he wouldn't go to sleep anywhere but in his basket. (That was before she knew the change Minna could produce.) So it came about that Peter slept – I suspect uneasily – on the mat outside her bedroom door. Then one day my wife said, '*Poor* Peter! No wonder he looks unhappy. He hasn't got his basket.' So the basket was dug out of the pile of miscellaneous kit which was awaiting disposal in the new house, and was ceremoniously put outside the door for Peter's accommodation. I rather liked the look of it and reflected aloud, to my wife's indignation, that Minna Minna Mowbray could just do with a basket like that.

Peter wagged his stump, looked intelligent and barked. That night he occupied the basket according to plan. We knew something was wrong (from Peter's point of view) when he scratched at the door the next morning about an hour before his usual time. He came in with the air of an ill-used dog, his stump registering dejection.

We had not long to wait for the explanation. Shortly after tea Minna Minna Mowbray stalked upstairs and leisurely installed herself in the basket. By the time we turned off the radio and went upstairs to bed she was coiled up fast asleep (or ostensibly so) while Peter, squatting on the landing, regarded her balefully from a discreet distance.

That was the beginning of the basket war. The old Trojan War, the Hundred Years War, and the Great War faded into insignificance. Our household was promptly divided into two factions – the pro-Peterites, led by my wife, and the pro-Minnaites, which was me. The cook thought it was too bad, the parlourmaid echoed, 'Poor Peter.' It is true the postman grinned unsympathetically when he heard about it, but he and Peter are traditional enemies, so that he was more anti-Peter than pro-Minna.

The fact that numbers were against her did not daunt my Minna. Her tiny stature was deceptive. In action she could give points to any Amazon. So that Peter's fugitive attempts to regain possession of his sleeping quarters are scarcely worth recording. Except perhaps the day when, bloated with tea and Dutch courage, he made a spirited attempt to get in while Minna dozed peacefully on the cushion. The battle was swiftly over; and Peter emerged from the regions of the coal cellar only after an interval of two days and much coaxing.

Then other and more important domestic affairs took precedence over the Minna–Peter feud. While the rest of the household talked of other things it rumbled on in a state of trench warfare, with Minna securely dug in and Peter making occasional raids across no-man's-landing. Indeed, we all regarded the basket war as a permanent feature of our domestic life.

Actually it lasted for just over two years. Armistice was declared only when our baby daughter Shirley crawled out of the bedroom door, seized Minna by the scruff of her furry neck, neatly ejected her and solemnly climbed into the basket.

Peter was present at the ceremony and (presumably) gave a loud doggy guffaw. Minna withdrew with dignity. She then turned the day nursery into her sleeping quarters and Peter retired to the kitchen. The basket was 'reconstructed' after the war and for a long time was occupied by a teddy bear, a musical duck and a woolly rabbit. There was peace in our time.

The other occasion when Minna graciously surrendered was the advent of Charles O'Malley, my Siamese cat. I have written another book about Charles and I shall not say much about him here; although readers of that book may understand my feeling that this is Hamlet without the Prince of Denmark.

Charles O'Malley was the first Siamese I had had. Minna Minna Mowbray was furious when I brought him home and always looked upon him as an intruder. It was quite clear that she would never forgive me for adopting another cat. As for Charles himself, Minna at first swore and spat vigorously at his approach. But she soon decided to tolerate him and after a fortnight or so the two cats were drinking peaceably from the same saucer. Charles, as a ten-weeks-old kitten, was enormously impressed by Minna Minna Mowbray. No amount of bad language or threats deterred him from the pursuit of her tail but it was several weeks before Minna permitted him to play with her.

Charles O'Malley was aristocratically bred, and looked it. With his sapphire-blue eyes, delicate cream coat, chocolate-pointed ears, feet, tail, and 'mask', he was a truly handsome creature.

There are differences between Siamese and other cats, apart from their shape and colouring. The Siamese voice is quite distinctive. When Minna first heard Charles' raucous squeak she visibly shuddered. Siamese cats have the reputation of being ferocious fighters; they are certainly stronger than ordinary cats. I do not think they are so graceful when walking or jumping. Indeed, Charles would land on his feet with a thud which was positively canine. Siamese are exquisite animals, however; sensitive, intelligent and responsive. Charles O'Malley (whom I confess I adopted partly to annoy Minna, who had been treating me very cavalierly at the time) was indeed a most lovable and charming cat and as readers of his story* will know, he was destined to become my best loved cat.

However, no despot ever ruled his kingdom with more certainty of getting his own way than Minna Minna Mowbray did the house which we then lived in. It was a benevolent tyranny, this rule of Minna's; often amusing, never malicious, always sure and precise. She was clearly a believer in the divine right of cats, exercising her power with due regard to the niceties and obligations of her position.

To the uninitiated it may appear that I was merely foolish about my cat. However, I was not Minna's only subject. She bossed everyone in the house, with the exception of my little daughter Shirley, who occasionally did a bit of bossing herself. But Minna was quite happy about

* *Charles: The Story of a Friendship*

that. Shirley was privileged to stroke her fur the wrong way, to play with her tail and to carry her round the nursery suspended at all sorts of queer angles. I fancy that Minna rather enjoyed it all. Shirley was very fond of her and if Minna was accidentally hurt when they were playing together – this rarely happened, for Shirley knew she must be careful – the ensuing ceremony of contrite apology on the part of one and the gracious forgiveness of the other was delightful to watch.

When Minna had kittens Shirley was a privileged visitor from the time of their birth. Minna allowed her to stroke them, knowing that Shirley would only touch them with gentleness. As soon as the babies reached the romping age Shirley was in her element. The nursery was transformed into an arena, in which young tigers leaped and raced swiftly in all directions, with Shirley's attempts at pursuit interrupted by her gurgles of excited laughter. Minna used to look on quite happily at these performances.

Like all cats who are happily accommodated in a human household Minna was a docile creature. But she insisted on having her own way. She would observe, with well-bred interest, my wife's painstaking preparations to provide her with a comfortable and secluded bed for her kittens. A large cardboard box, of the kind she loved, carefully lined with successive layers of newspaper, tissue paper and soft linen, and placed in one of her favourite cupboards, which was conveniently warm, well ventilated and discreetly dark – this was dutifully prepared at certain times by one of us. Whoever prepared her bed, however comfortably made and conveniently placed it might be, we could be sure of one thing – Minna would not use it.

Minna deceived several generations of interested cooks and house-parlourmaids by her tactics on these occasions. It was her custom to inspect at intervals the box or basket which had been so thoughtfully made ready for her, even to occupy it for forty winks every now and again as if to advertise her satisfaction. Many a beaming domestic servant announced the good news that 'Minnie is very pleased with her new box.' But these premature expectations were invariably disappointed. Minna knew what she was about. The attention of our expectant domestic staff being thus publicly drawn to a particular spot, Minna had her kittens elsewhere.

In this respect most cats, I believe, behave in the same independent way. Is it yet another survival of jungle instinct, this hiding away from prying eyes at important times? Or merely a gesture of independence, a rejection of our human proprietorship, a challenge to man and his stupid ways? Minna, although intensely secretive about her plans, made no further attempt at concealment when her kittens were born. She was then embarrassingly anxious that they should be seen and admired. In this I think she may have differed from other cats who, reasonably enough, do not like to be disturbed for some days. Minna, however, scorned further camouflage. She unmistakably invited us to pay our respects to the new arrivals. Nor did she object to their being touched. Our praise was clearly to her liking; she would purr loudly if we admired the little, squealing, almost invisible babies.

Naturally enough she would resent it if we overstayed our welcome, or if any stranger intruded on her privacy. And what a calamity if there should be any attempt to move her family! In that event, as soon as the coast was clear, Minna would remove them methodically, one by one, to what she obviously trusted would be a place less liable to disturbance. She was quite capable of registering a protest if disturbed by strangers; this usually took the form of depositing her kittens under the cover of my bed. There were times when I arrived home to find the house in a state of agitation because Minna and her kittens had disappeared. Nearly always they were to be found huddled together at the end of my bed comfortably asleep under the warm and sheltering darkness of the eiderdown.

Minna brooked no interference in her private affairs. At an early age she began to take an active interest in the opposite sex and all our well-meant efforts to influence her in the direction of a more lady-like modesty were frustrated. If the doors were shut she climbed out of a window. Nor were our attempts to find her a worthy husband any more successful. Whether the so-called attraction of opposites is responsible or not, it is a lamentable fact that Minna invariably chose the most disreputable gentleman friends. Any ugly, one-eyed, torn-eared tom-cat seemed to have an irresistible attraction for our Minna Minna Mowbray.

The uglier they were, the more eligible they appeared to be. She had, I remember, a disgraceful passion for an old roué with a lacerated tail, fractional ears, a permanently closed left eye and a pronounced limp. At his approach Minna behaved in a shameless and otherwise indescribable fashion. On such occasions I used to pretend she was not my cat.

When we were living in Surrey we did our best to reform her. It was not successful. Within a few days of our arrival the news had spread in some mysterious fashion that a new and comely lady cat had taken up her residence and that she had a decided preference for experienced lovers. Somehow Minna had made it known to the cats of all Surrey (and part of Sussex, too, I fancy) that she liked to choose her followers from the ranks of the veterans and middle-aged. She had no use for boy friends, it appeared.

We discovered this, and were considerably humiliated thereby, when we introduced her to a young orange cat from a neighbouring house. As soon as we set eyes on this cat, we decided that here was an ideal husband for Minna. He was a strikingly handsome cat, young and, so far as we could see, perfectly eligible. Minna, however, thought not. She promptly spat at him in a most unladylike way. Our candidate let us down badly. He fled for his life. After that we left Minna to her own devices – and to the reprobate toms of the neighbourhood.

To look at Minna Minna Mowbray as she sat demurely on the arm of my chair, her little white paws set neatly together in a modest pose, you would never imagine that she favoured the toughs and tramps of the tom-cat world.

In every other respect she was fastidious to the point of absurdity. She would refuse to drink from a saucer that was not spotlessly clean; would spend hours industriously making her toilet, until every hair was in its proper place; insisted on her milk being at exactly the right temperature; and objected to being touched, making a pretence of exquisite discomfort if I happened to stroke her when she didn't feel like it or to lay hands, however gently, on any part of her sensitive anatomy. Yet, ten minutes later, she could be observed (if you cared to gaze on the unedifying spectacle) in the garden below, being rolled playfully about in the mud by a cave-man lover from the slums of Camden Town.

My Cats

by Buster Lloyd-Jones

Pandora was a Siamese cat who thought she was a dachshund.

She came to me extremely sick, sent by people I didn't know and couldn't trace. Later I found that a judge had given her to his son and daughter-in-law. They had gone off on holiday, leaving the poor thing locked in an expensive flat in Belgravia with a few bottles of milk with the tops off and some opened tins of cat food. They were away for weeks and when the cat was found at last she was in a pitiful state.

When she came to see me she was so ill that for four weeks she would neither eat nor drink. The stamina of animals can be astonishing. She became a skeleton, poor creature, unable to move but she was still alive.

We gave her crushed garlic, honey and water, as much sun as possible and a lot of love, and very, very slowly she began to take an interest in life again. All her life she had been cooped up in a small flat and had seen few, if any, dogs before. Now she attached herself to a paralysed dachshund and shared his basket and it was touching to see the love these two sick animals had for each other.

The owners never got in touch with me again, thinking, no doubt, she was dead, and so she stayed. She grew into a sweet, lovely creature but to the end of her life she clearly believed she was a dachshund herself and only seemed really happy with dachshunds round her. We never had the heart to tell her . . .

Soon afterwards two more Siamese cats joined us. Their names were John and Josephine. They came to me after the divorce of their owners. They had gone with the wife who adored them – but she had had to go back to work and couldn't look after them. She asked if I would keep them for the time being. I agreed, and they duly arrived. Before she left, their owner gave elaborate instructions about food and exercise to the kennel maid and left with words that became famous at Dene's. 'They'll be all right,' she said, 'just as long as they never meet a dog . . .'

Well, of course you couldn't be at Dene's Close for five minutes without meeting dogs, much to the pleasure of John and Josephine. They were, in fact, more like dogs than cats. They played with the dogs for hour after hour and at night they slept in their kennels.

I had both for the rest of their lives – John for nine years and Josephine for twelve. They were always together but they were, as actresses say to airport reporters, just good friends.

Where love was concerned Josephine ignored poor John completely. She preferred a neighbouring ginger tom whom we all called Ginger Rogers. She produced litter after litter – and always the father was Ginger. I was always hoping for at least one pure-bred Siamese litter, if only as a boost for John's ego, but it was Ginger who had the sex-appeal.

Every now and then Josephine got asthma – sometimes quite badly. She would wheeze away and go very thin and look quite dreadful. I would be able to ease the discomfort, but asthma is a tricky thing to deal with and Josephine had these attacks all her life.

Just before Christmas one year a school teacher who lived nearby called in for some advice. She had found this pathetic Siamese cat, she said, absolutely starving. She seemed to be in a very bad way. What should she do? I gave her advice about feeding the cat up and putting it back into condition with powders and vitamins and she went her way.

A few days later she was back to borrow a cat basket. She was going to Exeter for Christmas, she said, and she would have to take the poor cat with her.

That night I couldn't find Josephine anywhere. She had

been in and out of the surgery wheezing away with asthma all morning, but no one had seen her since.

Suddenly the penny dropped. The teacher's starved Siamese was asthmatic Josephine, who had got on to a good thing. She had eaten her usual hearty dinner at Dene's and had popped out for another hearty meal across the garden...

I rang the teacher at once. Too late. She had already left for Exeter, taking Josephine with her. I was a bit worried about Josephine's asthma and anyway we wanted her home for Christmas, so I got the teacher's holiday address and rang her up.

'You know that half-starved Siamese?' I said. 'Well, her name is Josephine and she belongs to me. Could I have her back, please?'

Josephine arrived back next day. We put the basket on the surgery table, opened it and out she jumped looking marvellous. Her asthma had passed and she was sleek and handsome and delighted to be home again. She purred and rubbed herself against us, was unusually affectionate to John and then made for the kennels to sleep it off.

The Story of Webster

by P. G. Wodehouse

'Cats are not dogs!'

There is only one place where you can hear good things like that thrown off quite casually in the general run of conversation, and that is the bar parlour of the Angler's Rest. It was there, as we sat grouped about the fire, that a thoughtful Pint of Bitter had made the statement just recorded.

Although the talk up to this point had been dealing with Einstein's Theory of Relativity, we readily adjusted our minds to cope with the new topic. Regular attendance at the nightly sessions over which Mr Mulliner presides with such unfailing dignity and geniality tends to produce mental nimbleness. In our little circle I have known an argument on the Final Destination of the Soul to change inside forty seconds into one concerning the best method of preserving the juiciness of bacon fat.

'Cats,' proceeded the Pint of Bitter, 'are selfish. A man waits on a cat hand and foot for weeks, humouring its lightest whim, and then it goes and leaves him flat because it has found a place down the road where the fish is more frequent.'

'What I've got against cats,' said a Lemon Sour, speaking feelingly, as one brooding on a private grievance, 'is their unreliability. They lack candour and are not square shooters. You get your cat and you call him Thomas or George, as the case may be. So far, so good. Then one morning you wake up and find six kittens in the hat-box and you have to reopen the whole matter, approaching it from an entirely different angle.'

'If you want to know what's the trouble with cats,' said a

red-faced man with glassy eyes, who had been rapping on the table for his fourth whisky, 'they've got no tact. That's what's the trouble with them. I remember a friend of mine had a cat. Made quite a pet of that cat, he did. And what occurred? What was the outcome? One night he came home rather late and was feeling for the keyhole with his cork-screw; and, believe me or not, his cat selected that precise moment to jump on the back of his neck out of a tree. No tact.'

Mr Mulliner shook his head.

'I grant you all this,' he said, 'but still, in my opinion, you have not got to the root of the matter. The real objection to the great majority of cats is their insufferable air of superiority. Cats, as a class, have never completely got over the snootiness caused by the fact that in Ancient Egypt they were worshipped as gods. This makes them too prone to set themselves up as critics and censors of the frail and erring human beings whose lot they share. They stare rebukingly. They view with concern. And on a sensitive man this often has the worst effects, inducing an inferiority complex of the gravest kind. It is odd that the conversation should have taken this turn,' said Mr Mulliner, sipping his hot Scotch and lemon, 'for I was thinking only this afternoon of the rather strange case of my cousin Edward's son, Lancelot.'

'I knew a cat—' began a Small Bass.

My cousin Edward's son, Lancelot (said Mr Mulliner) was, at the time of which I speak, a comely youth of some twenty-five summers. Orphaned at an early age, he had been brought up in the home of his Uncle Theodore, the saintly Dean of Bolsover; and it was a great shock to that good man when Lancelot, on attaining his majority, wrote from London to inform him that he had taken a studio in Bott Street, Chelsea, and proposed to remain in the metropolis and become an artist.

The Dean's opinion of artists was low. As a prominent member of the Bolsover Watch Committee, it had recently been his distasteful duty to be present at a private showing of the super-super-film, *Palettes of Passion*; and he replied to his nephew's communication with a vibrant letter in which he emphasized the grievous pain it gave him to think that one of his flesh and blood should deliberately be embarking on a career which must inevitably lead sooner or later to the painting of Russian princesses lying on divans in the semi-nude with their arms round tame jaguars. He urged Lancelot to return and become a curate while there was yet time.

But Lancelot was firm. He deplored the rift between himself and a relative whom he had always respected; but he was dashed if he meant to go back to an environment where his individuality had been stifled and his soul confined in chains. And for four years there was silence between uncle and nephew.

During these years Lancelot had made progress in his chosen profession. At the time at which this story opens, his prospects seemed bright. He was painting the portrait of Brenda, only daughter of Mr and Mrs B. B. Carberry-Pirbright, of 11 Maxton Square, South Kensington, which meant thirty pounds in his sock on delivery. He had learned to cook eggs and bacon. He had practically mastered the ukulele. And, in addition, he was engaged to be married to a fearless young *vers libre* poetess of the name of Gladys Bingley, better known as The Sweet Singer of Garbidge Mews, Fulham – a charming girl who looked like a penwiper.

It seemed to Lancelot that life was very full and beautiful. He lived joyously in the present, giving no thought to the past.

But how true it is that the past is inextricably mixed up with the present and that we can never tell when it may spring some delayed bomb beneath our feet. One afternoon, as he sat making a few small alterations in the portrait of Brenda Carberry-Pirbright, his fiancée entered.

He had been expecting her to call, for today she was going off for a three weeks' holiday to the South of France, and she had promised to look in on her way to the station. He laid down his brush and gazed at her with a yearning affection, thinking for the thousandth time how he worshipped every spot of ink on her nose. Standing there in the doorway with her bobbed hair sticking out in every direction like a golliwog's, she made a picture that seemed to speak to his very depths.

'Hullo, Reptile!' he said lovingly.

'What ho, Worm!' said Gladys, maidenly devotion shining through the monocle which she wore in her left eye. 'I can stay just half an hour.'

'Oh, well, half an hour soon passes,' said Lancelot. 'What's that you've got there?'

'A letter, ass. What did you think it was?'

'Where did you get it?'

'I found the postman outside.'

Lancelot took the envelope from her and examined it.

'Gosh!' he said.

'What's the matter?'

'It's from my Uncle Theodore.'

'I didn't know you had an Uncle Theodore.'

'Of course I have. I've had him for years.'

'What's he writing to you about?'

'If you'll kindly keep quiet for two seconds, if you know how,' said Lancelot, 'I'll tell you.'

And in a clear voice which, like that of all the Mulliners, however distant from the main branch, was beautifully modulated, he read as follows:

The Deanery,
Bolsover, Wilts.

My dear Lancelot,

As you have, no doubt, already learned from your *Church Times*, I have been offered and have accepted the vacant Bishopric of Bongo-Bongo, in West Africa. I sail immediately to take up my new duties, which I trust will be blessed.

In these circumstances it becomes necessary for me to find a good home for my cat Webster. It is, alas, out of the question that he should accompany me, as the rigours of the climate and the lack of essential comforts might well sap a constitution which has never been robust.

I am dispatching him, therefore, to your address, my dear boy, in a straw-lined hamper, in the full confidence that you will prove a kindly and conscientious host.

With cordial good wishes,

Your affectionate uncle,

THEODORE BONGO-BONGO

For some moments after he had finished reading this communication, a thoughtful silence prevailed in the studio. Finally Gladys spoke.

'Of all the nerve!' she said. 'I wouldn't do it.'

'Why not?'

'What do you want with a cat?'

Lancelot reflected.

'It is true,' he said, 'that, given a free hand, I would prefer not to have my studio turned into a cattery or cat-bin. But consider the special circumstances. Relations between Uncle Theodore and self have for the last few years been a bit strained. In fact, you might say we had definitely parted brass-rags. It looks to me as if he were coming round. I should describe this letter as more or less what you might call an olive-branch. If I lush this cat up satisfactorily, shall I not be in a position later on to make a swift touch?'

'He is rich, this bean?' said Gladys, interested.

'Extremely.'

'Then,' said Gladys, 'consider my objections withdrawn. A good stout cheque from a grateful cat-fancier would undoubtedly come in very handy. We might be able to get married this year.'

'Exactly,' said Lancelot. 'A pretty loathsome prospect, of course; but still, as we've arranged to do it, the sooner we get it over, the better, what?'

'Absolutely.'

'Then that's settled. I accept custody of cat.'

'It's the only thing to do,' said Gladys. 'Meanwhile, can

you lend me a comb? Have you such a thing in your bedroom?'

'What do you want with a comb?'

'I got some soup in my hair at lunch. I won't be a minute.'

She hurried out, and Lancelot, taking up the letter again, found that he had omitted to read a continuation of it on the back page.

It was to the following effect:

PS. In establishing Webster in your home, I am actuated by another motive than the simple desire to see to it that my faithful friend and companion is adequately provided for.

From both a moral and an educative standpoint, I am convinced that Webster's society will prove of inestimable value to you. His advent, indeed, I venture to hope, will be a turning-point in your life. Thrown, as you must be, incessantly among loose and immoral Bohemians, you will find in this cat an example of upright conduct which cannot but act as an antidote to the poison cup of temptation which is, no doubt, hourly pressed to your lips.

PPS. Cream only at midday, and fish not more than three times a week.

He was reading these words for the second time, when the front doorbell rang and he found a man on the steps with a hamper. A discreet mew from within revealed its contents, and Lancelot, carrying it into the studio, cut the strings.

'Hi!' he bellowed, going to the door.

'What's up?' shrieked his betrothed from above.

'The cat's come.'

'All right. I'll be down in a jiffy.'

Lancelot returned to the studio.

'What ho, Webster!' he said cheerily. 'How's the boy?'

The cat did not reply. It was sitting with bent head, performing that wash and brush up which a journey by rail renders so necessary.

In order to facilitate these toilet operations, it had raised its left leg and was holding it rigidly in the air. And there flashed into Lancelot's mind an old superstition handed on

to him, for what it was worth, by one of the nurses of his infancy. If, this woman had said, you creep up to a cat when its leg is in the air and give it a pull, then you make a wish and your wish comes true in thirty days.

It was a pretty fancy, and it seemed to Lancelot that the theory might as well be put to the test. He advanced warily, therefore, and was in the act of extending his fingers for the pull, when Webster, lowering the leg, turned and raised his eyes.

He looked at Lancelot. And suddenly with sickening force there came to Lancelot the realization of the unpardonable liberty he had been about to take.

Until this moment, though the postscript to his uncle's letter should have warned him, Lancelot Mulliner had had no suspicion of what manner of cat this was that he had taken into his home. Now, for the first time, he saw him steadily and saw him whole.

Webster was very large and very black and very composed. He conveyed the impression of being a cat of deep reserves. Descendant of a long line of ecclesiastical ancestors who had conducted their decorous courtships beneath the shadow of cathedrals and on the back walls of bishops' palaces, he had that exquisite poise which one sees in high dignitaries of the Church. His eyes were clear and steady, and seemed to pierce to the very roots of the young man's soul, filling him with a sense of guilt.

Once, long ago, in his hot childhood, Lancelot, spending his summer holidays at the deanery, had been so far carried away by ginger-beer and original sin as to plug a senior canon in the leg with his air-gun – only to discover, on turning, that a visiting archdeacon had been a spectator of the entire incident from his immediate rear. As he had felt then, when meeting the archdeacon's eye, so did he feel now as Webster's gaze played silently upon him.

Webster, it is true, had not actually raised his eyebrows. But this, Lancelot felt, was simply because he hadn't any.

He backed, blushing.

'Sorry!' he muttered.

There was a pause. Webster continued his steady scrutiny. Lancelot edged towards the door.

'Er – excuse me – just a moment . . .' he mumbled. And, sidling from the room, he ran distractedly upstairs.

'I say,' said Lancelot.

'Now what?' asked Gladys.

'Have you finished with the mirror?'

'Why?'

'Well, I – er – I thought,' said Lancelot, 'that I might as well have a shave.'

The girl looked at him, astonished.

'Shave? Why, you shaved only the day before yesterday.'

'I know. But, all the same . . . I mean to say, it seems only respectful. That cat, I mean.'

'What about him?'

'Well, he seems to expect it, somehow. Nothing actually said, don't you know, but you could tell by his manner. I thought a quick shave and perhaps change into my blue serge suit—'

'He's probably thirsty. Why don't you give him some milk?'

'Could one, do you think?' said Lancelot doubtful. 'I mean, I hardly seem to know him well enough.' He paused. 'I say, old girl,' he went on, with a touch of hesitation.

'Hullo?'

'I know you won't mind my mentioning it, but you've got a few spots of ink on your nose.'

'Of course I have. I always have spots of ink on my nose.'

'Well . . . you don't think . . . a quick scrub with a bit of pumice-stone . . . I mean to say, you know how important first impressions are . . .'

The girl stared.

'Lancelot Mulliner,' she said, 'if you think I'm going to skin my nose to the bone just to please a mangy cat—'

'Sh!' cried Lancelot, in agony.

'Here, let me go down and look at him,' said Gladys petulantly.

As they re-entered the studio, Webster was gazing with an

air of quiet distaste at an illustration from *La Vie Parisienne* which adorned one of the walls. Lancelot tore it down hastily.

Gladys looked at Webster in an unfriendly way.

'So that's the blighter!'

'Sh!'

'If you want to know what I think,' said Gladys, 'that cat's been living too high. Doing himself a dashed sight too well. You'd better cut his rations down a bit.'

In substance, her criticism was not unjustified. Certainly, there was about Webster more than a suspicion of *embonpoint*. He had that air of portly well-being which we associate with those who dwell in cathedral closes. But Lancelot winced uncomfortably. He had so hoped that Gladys would make a good impression, and here she was, starting right off by saying the tactless thing.

He longed to explain to Webster that it was only her way; that in the Bohemian circles of which she was such an ornament genial chaff of a personal order was accepted and, indeed, relished. But it was too late. The mischief had been done. Webster turned in a pointed manner and withdrew silently behind the chesterfield.

Gladys, all unconscious, was making preparations for departure.

'Well, bung-oh,' she said lightly. 'See you in three weeks. I suppose you and that cat'll both be out on the tiles the moment my back's turned.'

'Please! Please!' moaned Lancelot. 'Please!'

He had caught sight of the tip of a black tail protruding from behind the chesterfield. It was twitching slightly, and Lancelot could read it like a book. With a sickening sense of dismay, he knew that Webster had formed a snap judgement of his fiancée and condemned her as frivolous and unworthy.

It was some ten days later that Bernard Worple, the neo-Vorticist sculptor, lunching at the Puce Ptarmigan, ran into Rodney Scollop, the powerful young surrealist. And after talking for a while of their art:

'What's all this I hear about Lancelot Mulliner?' asked Worple. 'There's a wild story going about that he was seen shaved in the middle of the week. Nothing in it, I suppose?'

Scollop looked grave. He had been on the point of mentioning Lancelot himself, for he loved the lad and was deeply exercised about him.

'It is perfectly true,' he said.

'It sounds incredible.'

Scollop leaned forward. His fine face was troubled.

'Shall I tell you something, Worple?'

'What?'

'I know for an absolute fact,' said Scollop, 'that Lancelot Mulliner now shaves every morning.'

Worple pushed aside the spaghetti which he was wreathing about him and through the gap stared at his companion.

'Every morning?'

'Every single morning. I looked in on him myself the other day, and there he was, neatly dressed in blue serge and shaved to the core. And, what is more, I got the distinct impression that he had used talcum powder afterwards.'

'You don't mean that!'

'I do. And shall I tell you something else? There was a book lying open on the table. He tried to hide it, but he wasn't quick enough. It was one of those etiquette books!'

'An etiquette book!'

'*Polite Behaviour*, by Constance, Lady Bodbank.'

Worple unwound a stray tendril of spaghetti from about his left ear. He was deeply agitated. Like Scollop, he loved Lancelot.

'He'll be dressing for dinner next!' he exclaimed.

'I have every reason to believe,' said Scollop gravely, 'that he does dress for dinner. At any rate, a man closely resembling him was seen furtively buying three stiff collars and a black tie at Hope Brothers in the King's Road last Tuesday.'

Worple pushed his chair back, and rose. His manner was determined.

'Scollop,' he said, 'we are friends of Mulliner's, you and

I. It is evident from what you tell me that subversive influences are at work and that never has he needed our friendship more. Shall we not go round and see him immediately?'

'It was what I was about to suggest myself,' said Rodney Scollop.

Twenty minutes later they were in Lancelot's studio, and with a significant glance Scollop drew his companion's notice to their host's appearance. Lancelot Mulliner was neatly, even foppishly, dressed in blue serge with creases down the trouser-legs, and his chin, Worple saw with a pang, gleamed smoothly in the afternoon light.

At the sight of his friends' cigars, Lancelot exhibited unmistakable concern.

'You don't mind throwing those away, I'm sure,' he said pleadingly.

Rodney Scollop drew himself up a little haughtily.

'And since when,' he asked, 'have the best fourpenny cigars in Chelsea not been good enough for you?'

Lancelot hastened to soothe him.

'It isn't me,' he exclaimed. 'It's Webster. My cat. I happen to know he objects to tobacco smoke. I had to give up my pipe in deference to his views.'

Bernard Worple snorted.

'Are you trying to tell us,' he sneered, 'that Lancelot Mulliner allows himself to be dictated to by a blasted cat?'

'Hush!' cried Lancelot, trembling. 'If you knew how he disapproves of strong language!'

'Where is this cat?' asked Rodney Scollop. 'Is that the animal?' he said, pointing out of the window to where, in the yard, a tough-looking Tom with tattered ears stood mewing in a hard-boiled way out of the corner of its mouth.

'Good heavens, no!' said Lancelot. 'That is an alley cat which comes round here from time to time to lunch at the dustbin. Webster is quite different. Webster has a natural dignity and repose of manner. Webster is a cat who prides himself on always being well turned out and whose high principles and lofty ideals shine from his eyes like beacon fires . . .' And then suddenly, with an abrupt change of manner, Lancelot broke down and in a low voice added: 'Curse him! Curse him! Curse him! Curse him!'

Worple looked at Scollop. Scollop looked at Worple.

'Come, old man,' said Scollop, laying a gentle hand on Lancelot's bowed shoulder. 'We are your friends. Confide in us.'

'Tell us all,' said Worple. 'What's the matter?'

Lancelot uttered a bitter, mirthless laugh.

'You want to know what's the matter? Listen, then. I'm cat-pecked!'

'Cat-pecked?'

'You've heard of men being hen-pecked, haven't you?' said Lancelot with a touch of irritation. 'Well, I'm cat-pecked.'

And in broken accents he told his story. He sketched the history of his association with Webster from the latter's first entry into the studio. Confident now that the animal was not within earshot, he unbosomed himself without reserve.

'It's something in the beast's eye,' he said in a shaking voice. 'Something hypnotic. He casts a spell upon me. He gazes at me and disapproves. Little by little, bit by bit, I am degenerating under his influence from a wholesome, self-respecting artist into . . . well, I don't know what you call it. Suffice it to say that I have given up smoking, that I have ceased to wear carpet slippers and go about without a collar, that I never dream of sitting down to my frugal evening meal without dressing, and' – he choked – 'I have sold my ukulele.'

'Not that!' said Worple, paling.

'Yes,' said Lancelot. 'I felt he considered it frivolous.'

There was a long silence.

'Mulliner,' said Scollop, 'this is more serious than I had supposed. We must brood upon your case.'

'It may be possible,' said Worple, 'to find a way out.'

Lancelot shook his head hopelessly.

'There is no way out. I have explored every avenue. The only thing that could possibly free me from this intolerable bondage would be if once – just once – I could catch that cat unbending. If once – merely once – it would lapse in my presence from its austere dignity for but a single instant, I feel that the spell would be broken. But what hope is there of that?' cried Lancelot passionately. 'You were pointing just now to that alley cat in the yard. There stands one who has strained every nerve and spared no effort to break down Webster's inhuman self-control. I have heard that animal say things to him which you would think no cat with red blood in its veins would suffer for an instant. And Webster merely looks at him like a Suffragan Bishop eyeing an erring choirboy and turns his head and falls into a refreshing sleep.'

He broke off with a dry sob. Worple, always an optimist, attempted in his kindly way to minimize the tragedy.

'Ah, well,' he said. 'It's bad, of course, but still, I suppose there is no actual harm in shaving and dressing for dinner and so on. Many great artists . . . Whistler, for example—'

'Wait!' cried Lancelot. 'You have not heard the worst.'

He rose feverishly, and, going to the easel, disclosed the portrait of Brenda Carberry-Pirbright.

'Take a look at that,' he said, 'and tell me what you think of her.'

His two friends surveyed the face before them in silence. Miss Carberry-Pirbright was a young woman of prim and glacial aspect. One sought in vain for her reasons for wanting to have her portrait painted. It would be a most unpleasant thing to have about any house.

Scollop broke the silence.

'Friend of yours?'

'I can't stand the sight of her,' said Lancelot vehemently.

'Then,' said Scollop, 'I may speak frankly. I think she's a pill.'

'A blister,' said Worple.

'A boil and a disease,' said Scollop, summing up.

Lancelot laughed hackingly.

'You have described her to a nicety. She stands for everything most alien to my artist soul. She gives me a pain in the neck. I'm going to marry her.'

'What!' cried Scollop.

'But you're going to marry Gladys Bingley,' said Worple.

'Webster thinks not,' said Lancelot bitterly. 'At their first meeting he weighed Gladys in the balance and found her wanting. And the moment he saw Brenda Carberry-Pirbright he stuck his tail up at right angles, uttered a cordial gargle, and rubbed his head against her leg. Then turning, he looked at me. I could read that glance. I knew what was in his mind. From that moment he has been doing everything in his power to arrange the match.'

'But, Mulliner,' said Worple, always eager to point out the bright side, 'why should this girl want to marry a wretched, scrubby, hard-up footler like you? Have courage, Mulliner. It is simply a question of time before you repel and sicken her.'

Lancelot shook his head.

'No,' he said. 'You speak like a true friend, Worple, but you do not understand. Old Ma Carberry-Pirbright, this exhibit's mother, who chaperons her at the sittings, discovered at an early date my relationship to my Uncle Theodore, who, as you know, has got it in gobs. She knows well enough that some day I shall be a rich man. She used to know my Uncle Theodore when he was Vicar of St Botolph's in Knightsbridge, and from the very first she assumed towards me the repellent chumminess of an old family friend. She was always trying to lure me to her At Homes, her Sunday luncheons, her little dinners. Once she actually suggested that I should escort her and her beastly daughter to the Royal Academy.'

He laughed bitterly. The mordant witticisms of Lancelot Mulliner at the expense of the Royal Academy were quoted from Tite Street in the south to Holland Park in the north and eastward as far as Bloomsbury.

'To all these overtures,' resumed Lancelot, 'I remained firmly unresponsive. My attitude was from the start one of frigid aloofness. I did not actually say in so many words that I would rather be dead in a ditch than at one of her At Homes, but my manner indicated it. And I was just beginning to think I had choked her off when in crashed Webster and upset everything. Do you know how many times I have been to that infernal house in the last week? Five. Webster seemed to wish it. I tell you, I am a lost man.'

He buried his face in his hands. Scollop touched Worple on the arm, and together the two men stole silently out.

'Bad!' said Worple.

'Very bad,' said Scollop.

'It seems incredible.'

'Oh, no. Cases of this kind are, alas, by no means uncommon among those who, like Mulliner, possess to a marked degree the highly-strung, ultra-sensitive artistic temperament. A friend of mine, a rhythmical interior decorator, once rashly consented to put his aunt's parrot up at his studio while she was away visiting friends in the north of England. She was a woman of strong evangelical views, which the bird had imbibed from her. It had a way of putting its head on one side, making a noise like someone drawing a cork from a bottle, and asking my friend if he was saved. To cut a long story short, I happened to call on him a month later and he had installed a harmonium in his studio and was singing hymns, ancient and modern, in a rich tenor, while the parrot, standing on one leg on its perch, took the bass. A very sad affair. We were all much upset about it.'

Worple shuddered.

'You appal me, Scollop! Is there nothing we can do?'

Rodney Scollop considered for a moment.

'We might wire Gladys Bingley to come home at once. She might possibly reason with the unhappy man. A woman's gentle influence . . . Yes, we could do that. Look in at the post office on your way home and send Gladys a telegram. I'll owe you for my half of it.'

In the studio they had left, Lancelot Mulliner was staring dumbly at a black shape which had just entered the room. He had the appearance of a man with his back to the wall.

'No!' he was crying. 'No! I'm dashed if I do!'

Webster continued to look at him.

'Why should I?' demanded Lancelot weakly.

Webster's gaze did not flicker.

'Oh, all right,' said Lancelot sullenly.

He passed from the room with leaden feet, and, proceeding upstairs, changed into morning clothes and a top hat. Then, with a gardenia in his buttonhole, he made his way to 11 Maxton Square, where Mrs Carberry-Pirbright was giving one of her intimate little teas ('just a few friends') to meet Clara Throckmorton Stooge, authoress of *A Strong Man's Kiss*.

Gladys Bingley was lunching at her hotel in Antibes when Worple's telegram arrived. It occasioned her the gravest concern.

Exactly what it was all about she was unable to gather, for emotion had made Bernard Worple rather incoherent. There were moments, reading it, when she fancied that Lancelot had met with a serious accident; others when the solution seemed to be that he had sprained his brain to such an extent that rival lunatic asylums were competing eagerly for his custom; others, again, when Worple appeared to be suggesting that he had gone into partnership with his cat to start a harem. But one fact emerged clearly. Her loved one was in serious trouble of some kind, and his best friends were agreed that only her immediate return could save him.

Gladys did not hesitate. Within half an hour of the receipt of the telegram she had packed her trunk, removed a piece of asparagus from her right eyebrow, and was negotiating for accommodation on the first train going north.

Arriving in London, her first impulse was to go straight to Lancelot. But a natural feminine curiosity urged her, before doing so, to call upon Bernard Worple and have light thrown on some of the more abstruse passages in the telegram.

Worple, in his capacity of author, may have tended towards obscurity, but, when confining himself to the spoken word, he told a plain story well and clearly. Five minutes of his society enabled Gladys to obtain a firm grasp on the salient facts, and there appeared on her face that grim, tight-lipped expression which is seen only on the faces of fiancées who have come back from a short holiday to discover that their dear one has been straying in their absence from the straight and narrow path.

'Brenda Carberry-Pirbright, eh?' said Gladys, with ominous calm. 'I'll give him Brenda Carberry-Pirbright! My gosh, if one can't go off to Antibes for the merest breather without having one's betrothed getting it up his nose and starting to act like a Mormon Elder, it begins to look a pretty tough world for a girl.'

Kind-hearted Bernard Worple did his best.

'I blame the cat,' he said. 'Lancelot, to my mind, is more sinned against than sinning. I consider him to be acting under undue influence or duress.'

'How like a man!' said Gladys. 'Shoving it all off on to an innocent cat!'

'Lancelot says it has a sort of something in its eye.'

'Well, when I meet Lancelot,' said Gladys, 'he'll find that I have a sort of something in my eye.'

She went out, breathing flame quietly through her nostrils. Worple, saddened, heaved a sigh and resumed his neo-Vorticist sculpting.

It was some five minutes later that Gladys, passing through Maxton Square on her way to Bott Street, stopped suddenly in her tracks. The sight she had seen was enough to make any fiancée do so.

Along the pavement leading to No 11 two figures were advancing. Or three, if you counted a morose-looking dog of a semi-dachshund nature which preceded them, attached to a leash. One of the figures was that of Lancelot Mulliner, natty in grey herring-bone tweed and a new Homburg hat. It was he who held the leash. The other Gladys recognized from the portrait which she had seen on Lancelot's easel as that modern Du Barry, that notorious wrecker of homes and breaker-up of love-nests, Brenda Carberry-Pirbright.

The next moment they had mounted the steps of No 11, and had gone in to tea, possibly with a little music.

It was perhaps an hour and a half later that Lancelot, having wrenched himself with difficulty from the lair of the Philistines, sped homeward in a swift taxi. As always after an extended *tête-à-tête* with Miss Carberry-Pirbright, he felt dazed and bewildered, as if he had been swimming in a sea of glue and had swallowed a good deal of it. All he could think of clearly was that he wanted a drink and that the materials for that drink were in the cupboard behind the chesterfield in his studio.

He paid the cab and charged in with his tongue rattling dryly against his front teeth. And there before him was Gladys Bingley, whom he had supposed far, far away.

'You!' exclaimed Lancelot.

'Yes, me!' said Gladys.

Her long vigil had not helped to restore the girl's equanimity. Since arriving at the studio she had had leisure to tap her foot three thousand, one hundred and forty-two times on the carpet, and the number of bitter smiles which had flitted across her face was nine hundred and eleven. She was about ready for the battle of the century.

She rose and faced him, all the woman in her flashing from her eyes.

'Well, you Casanova!' she said.

'You who?' said Lancelot.

'Don't say "Yoo-hoo!" to me!' cried Gladys. 'Keep that for your Brenda Carberry-Pirbright. Yes, I know all about it, Lancelot Don Juan Henry the Eighth Mulliner! I saw you with her just now. I hear that you and she are inseparable. Bernard Worple says you said you were going to marry her.'

'You mustn't believe everything a neo-Vorticist sculptor tells you,' quavered Lancelot.

'I'll bet you're going back to dinner there tonight,' said Gladys.

She had spoken at a venture, basing the charge purely on a possessive cock of the head which she had noticed in Brenda Carberry-Pirbright at their recent encounter. There, she had said to herself at the time, had gone a girl who was about to invite – or had just invited – Lancelot Mulliner to dine quietly and take her to the pictures afterwards. But the shot went home. Lancelot hung his head.

'There was some talk of it,' he admitted.

'Ah!' exclaimed Gladys.

Lancelot's eyes were haggard.

'I don't want to go,' he pleaded. 'Honestly, I don't. But Webster insists.'

'Webster!'

'Yes, Webster. If I attempt to evade the appointment, he will sit in front of me and look at me.'

'Tchah!'

'Well, he will. Ask him for yourself.'

Gladys tapped her foot six times in rapid succession on the carpet, bringing the total to three thousand, one hundred and forty-eight. Her manner had changed and was now dangerously calm.

'Lancelot Mulliner,' she said, 'you have your choice. Me, on the one hand, Brenda Carberry-Pirbright on the other. I offer you a home where you will be able to smoke in bed, spill the ashes on the floor, wear pyjamas and carpet slippers all day and shave only on Sunday mornings. From her, what have you to hope? A house in South Kensington – possibly the Brompton Road – probably with her mother living with you. A life that will be one long round of stiff collars and tight shoes, of morning coats and top hats.'

Lancelot quivered, but she went on remorselessly.

'You will be at home on alternate Thursdays, and will be expected to hand the cucumber sandwiches. Every day you will air the dog, till you become a confirmed dog-airer. You will dine out in Bayswater and go for the summer to Bournemouth or Dinard. Choose well, Lancelot Mulliner! I will leave you to think it over. But one last word. If by seven-thirty on the dot you have not presented yourself at 6a Garbidge Mews ready to take me out to dinner at the Ham and Beef, I shall know what to think and shall act accordingly.'

And brushing the cigarette ashes from her chin, the girl strode haughtily from the room.

'Gladys!' cried Lancelot.

But she had gone.

For some minutes Lancelot Mulliner remained where he was, stunned. Then, insistently, there came to him the recollection that he had not had that drink. He rushed to the cupboard and produced the bottle. He uncorked it, and was pouring out a lavish stream, when a movement on the floor below him attracted his attention.

Webster was standing there, looking up at him. And in his eyes was that familiar expression of quiet rebuke.

'Scarcely what I have been accustomed to at the Deanery,' he seemed to be saying.

Lancelot stood paralysed. The feeling of being bound hand and foot, of being caught in a snare from which there was no escape, had become more poignant than ever. The bottle fell from his nerveless fingers and rolled across the floor, spilling its contents in an amber river, but he was too heavy in spirit to notice it. With a gesture such as Job might have made on discovering a new boil, he crossed to the window and stood looking moodily out.

Then, turning with a sigh, he looked at Webster again – and, looking, stood spellbound.

The spectacle which he beheld was of a kind to stun a stronger man than Lancelot Mulliner. At first, he shrank from believing his eyes. Then, slowly, came the realization that what he saw was no mere figment of a disordered imagination. This unbelievable thing was actually happening.

Webster sat crouched upon the floor beside the widening pool of whisky. But it was not horror and disgust that had caused him to crouch. He was crouched because, crouching, he could get nearer to the stuff and obtain crisper action. His tongue was moving in and out like a piston.

And then abruptly, for one fleeting instant, he stopped lapping and glanced up at Lancelot, and across his face there flitted a quick smile – so genial, so intimate, so full of jovial camaraderie, that the young man found himself automatically smiling back, and not only smiling but winking. And in answer to that wink Webster winked too – a whole-hearted, roguish wink that said as plainly as if he had spoken the words:

'How long has this been going on?'

Then with a slight hiccough he turned back to the task of getting his drink before it soaked into the floor.

Into the murky soul of Lancelot Mulliner there poured a sudden flood of sunshine. It was as if a great burden had been lifted from his shoulders. The intolerable obsession of the last two weeks had ceased to oppress him, and he felt a free man. At the eleventh hour the reprieve had come. Webster, that seeming pillar of austere virtue, was one of the boys, after all. Never again would Lancelot quail beneath his eye. He had the goods on him.

Webster, like the stag at eve, had now drunk his fill. He had left the pool of alcohol and was walking round in slow, meditative circles. From time to time he mewed tentatively, as if he were trying to say 'British Constitution'. His failure to articulate the syllables appeared to tickle him, for at the end of each attempt he would utter a slow, amused chuckle. It was about this moment that he suddenly broke into a rhythmic dance, not unlike the old Saraband.

It was an interesting spectacle, and at any other time Lancelot would have watched it raptly. But now he was busy at his desk, writing a brief note to Mrs Carberry-Pirbright, the burden of which was that if she thought he was coming within a mile of her foul house that night or any other night she had vastly underrated the dodging powers of Lancelot Mulliner.

And what of Webster? The Demon Rum now had him in an iron grip. A lifetime of abstinence had rendered him a ready victim to the fatal fluid. He had now reached the stage when geniality gives way to belligerence. The rather foolish smile had gone from his face, and in its stead there lowered a fighting frown. For a few moments he stood on his hind legs, looking about him for a suitable adversary: then, losing all vestiges of self-control, he ran five times round the room at a high rate of speed and, falling foul of a small footstool, attacked it with the utmost ferocity, sparing neither tooth nor claw.

But Lancelot did not see him. Lancelot was not there. Lancelot was out in Bott Street, hailing a cab.

'6a Garbidge Mews, Fulham,' said Lancelot to the driver.

The Owl and the Pussy-Cat

by EDWARD LEAR

The Owl and the Pussy-Cat went to sea
In a beautiful pea-green boat,
They took some honey, and plenty of money,
Wrapped up in a five-pound note.

The Owl looked up to the stars above,
And sang to a small guitar,
'O lovely Pussy! O Pussy my love,
What a beautiful Pussy you are!'

Pussy said to the Owl, 'You elegant fowl!
How charmingly sweet you sing!
O! let us be married! Too long we have tarried:
But what shall we do for a ring?'

They sailed away for a year and a day,
To the land where the Bong-Tree grows,
And there in a wood a Piggy-Wig stood
With a ring at the end of his nose.

'Dear Pig are you willing, to sell for one shilling
Your ring?' Said the Piggy, 'I will,'
So they took it away and were married next day,
By the turkey who lives on the hill.

They dined on mince and slices of quince,
Which they ate with a runcible spoon,
And hand in hand, on the edge of the sand,
They danced by the light of the moon.

The Christmas Cat

by John Montgomery

For two more evenings Snowy went to the barn and slept in the same corner, close to the cattle trough, with her tail curled around her, away from draughts and intruders and strangers. The horses took no notice of her and she saw no one. There was no more perfect refuge; outside it was still snowing, inside it was warm and dry. When it grew dark she crept around the backs of the houses looking for scraps of food in the snow. Then she returned to her new home, usually still hungry. But on the third day something happened which was to alter her whole life; something extraordinary.

She had found an old piece of bread, and near to it a broken egg, which she considered quite a reasonable supper, and had just decided to go home, when the snow stopped falling. There was nothing remarkable about that, she hoped it would never start again. But what was unusual was that although by the time she started wending her way towards the barn it was quite late, almost midnight she thought, the sky was strangely bright. She had never before seen such a glow. All the houses and walls and rooftops stood out in clearest white, as if trying to match the snow. It was as if the whole village had been lit by a large lamp, which hung suspended above the houses.

When she came to the wall of the inn and jumped up to look down at the barn she knew at once that it was no longer her home. There was a light inside, and she could hear voices. Curious, she walked across the yard, jumped up to the window, and looked inside.

The two horses were still there, and there were now some oxen tied up in a stall at the far end. But what surprised her was that there were also people there, dim figures over in the corner. Noiselessly, she jumped down and crept over the straw to watch.

There was a man with a dark beard and there was a woman whose face was covered by a veil of white material. Snowy moved a little closer, and then to her surprise she saw, lying down on the straw over to her right, her friend the donkey from the next village. She went over to him at once.

'Hullo!' she said. 'Welcome! I didn't expect to see you here.'

He looked up, half asleep. 'Oh, it's you – and you're still white. My, what a night! I knew they'd want me to make the journey again. The young ones can't do it, they don't know the path, it's very tricky. It was quite a struggle. There was the woman, and all that baggage, and the man helping to guide me. But I flatter myself that I'm the only donkey in the district that could have brought them here. Once I thought we were going over, I slipped on a very dangerous corner, but we managed somehow. And guess what happened when we arrived?'

'What?'

'They said they were full up in the inn. No room. A whole lot of people have come over to take the census, to register all the names and addresses. They wouldn't let us in. Disgraceful, in her condition. We went to several other houses but no one wanted us. So we ended up here. It's the first time I've seen humans living in a stable, I don't know what things are coming to. They're very nice people, they gave me a good meal. You know, I'm dead tired, but I feel almost young again. I don't know how I managed to climb that hill, but we made it. It was almost as if something or someone *made* me get here, as if someone was pushing me, guiding my feet. They're not quite like any humans I've seen before. Go and have a look at them.'

Snowy walked over to the corner, and to her surprise she found that it was *her* alcove, her particular corner of the stable, that the family had taken over. The woman was bending over a small bundle wrapped in white linen and rugs. And as the cat watched she saw it was a baby; a tiny sleeping face, with a little dark hair on its head, and the veiled woman bending over it. So small it seemed, but never a murmur, never a cry.

As she watched she saw the man turn towards her and for a moment she felt afraid. But if he intended any harm he did not show it.

'Look,' he said, 'it's a white cat.'

The woman drew back her veil and raised her head, and as Snowy gazed at her she thought she had never seen such a beautiful face in her life.

'Isn't she pretty?' said the woman. 'I think this must be her home. Perhaps she won't mind us sharing it with her.'

For the first time in her life the cat was not afraid of humans. She knew instinctively that she would be perfectly safe with these people, and would even be wanted. They were quite different from the Roman soldiers on their horses, or the housewives with their brooms, or the boys who stoned her. So she walked forward on to the hay and curled herself up near the child's feet. It was a very small baby, and after all – it was *her* bed. And at that moment, as she settled herself down, just as your cat and mine have done countless times in front of the fire or in a quiet corner, something strange happened. Snowy's tail, moving round to be wrapped neatly around her body, accidentally brushed against the edge of the rug in which the child was wrapped. It was extraordinary – it seemed as if for a second every living creature, every man and animal and bird and fish and insect suddenly stood still; it was as if her heart had ceased to beat, as if she had just for that brief instant in her short life become something more than a small stray cat in a great hostile world; as if she were almost immortal. But it was for only a second, and such moments come to very few of us.

Snowy looked at the child, and the infant opened his tiny eyes. And as they looked at one another the green eyes of the cat met the dark brown eyes of the boy, and there was reflected between them all the promise and hopes of events and years yet to come – the far distant days when people would no longer throw stones, when unkindness and jealousy would give place to love and charity, when all men and women and animals would walk together in peace and understanding and dignity in an age of tolerance.

Snowy did not appreciate the meaning that lay behind those small brown eyes, but then she was only a cat. Certainly, she was not alone in her ignorance, because many millions of otherwise quite intelligent people have since failed to understand the message of those eyes. Yet it was there.

'Mary,' said the man, 'we have a visitor.'

From out of the darkness into the dim lamplight stepped a young man. His dark hair was long and tousled, he wore a rough coat of sheepskin, his sandals were old and worn, and he carried a stick. He was almost breathless from running, his bronzed face was wet and his blue eyes were bright, aflame.

'Am I the first?' he asked. 'We saw the angel in the field and then we saw the great star above the village and I ran all the way. The others are coming. I must be the first. And this must be . . .'

He walked forward and stood looking at the child, wrapped in its linen and rugs.

'Glory be,' he said, and kneeling down he began to pray. And presently his companions came and joined him, all kneeling in prayer before the child, while Mary and Joseph watched over Him.

When at last the young man rose to his feet he saw through his tears the small white cat with the green eyes, curled up in the straw.

'Ah,' he whispered, 'so I've found you again, Snowy. I was sure I would, one day.'

Picking her up in his arms he walked slowly out of the stable and down the hill to where the shepherds' black tents stood. The cat would never again be hungry or lonely or unwanted, she had found her home.

Behind them, above the village of Bethlehem, the great bright star shone out high in the heavens to guide pilgrims towards the stable. It stood out like a beacon above the world; the hope of all humanity and every living creature.

*

It is still there, if you care to look for it.

A story-teller whose inimitable style of humour, gentle satire and understanding has given pleasure to thousands of readers.

PAUL GALLICO

THE MAN WHO WAS MAGIC (*illustrated*) 5/-

To Mageia, the city of theatrical magicians, comes Adam—a young man with genuine magical powers. It is not long before his innocent and miraculous gift stirs up unrest...

'Mr. Gallico's theme... is full of the sort of magic that he has made his own'
OXFORD TIMES

MRS. HARRIS MP 3/6

'Live and Let Live' was Mrs Harris's slogan when she entered politics. But she soon realized that 'It takes more than wanting to 'elp people... You got to know 'ow'.

'No one who enjoys Paul Gallico's charming tales will be disappointed with this one'
HOUSEWIFE

LOVE, LET ME NOT HUNGER 5/-

There has never been a novel about the circus like this one, a story of disaster and eventual deliverance, and of the infinite variety of human emotion.

'Outstanding'
THE DAILY TELEGRAPH

THE HAND OF MARY CONSTABLE 5/-

A startling novel about the frightening use of psychic phenomena as a weapon in the Cold War.

'Hypnotic... a splendid thriller'
THE DAILY TELEGRAPH